HUMAN SYSTEMS

Martin Griffin

B.Sc (Hons), C. Biol., M.I.Biol., A.C.T. (Birm)
Teacher, lecturer in Physiology at Matthew
Boulton College in Birmingham, Chief
Examiner in A and AS Level Biology with a
major Examining Board, Assistant Chief
Examiner in GCSE Biology and Combined
Sciences with a major Examining Board

&

Alison Redmore

B.Sc. (Hons), P.G.C.E., C. Biol., M.I.Biol.
Teacher in the Cavendish School, Hemel
Hempstead, Chief Examiner in A and AS
Level Biology with a major Examining Board

Nelson

Nelson Blackie
Westercleddens Road
Bishopbriggs
Glasgow G64 2NZ

Thomas Nelson and Sons Ltd
Nelson House
Mayfield Road
Walton-on-Thames
Surrey KT12 5PL

51 York Place
Edinburgh EH1 3JD

Thomas Nelson Australia
102 Dodds Road
South Melbourne
Victoria 3205
Australia

Nelson Canada
1120 Birchmont Road
Scarborough
Ontario M1K 5G4
Canada

First published by Thomas Nelson and sons Ltd 1993
© Martin Griffin and Alison Redmore 1993

Front cover courtesy of Science Photo Library
Illustrated by David Gardner

ISBN 0-17-448199-3
NPN 9 8 7 6 5 4 3

ACKNOWLEDGEMENTS

The authors would like to acknowledge the help and advice of the following: Mr Trevor Watts and Mr John Hamilton, Manor Hospital, Walsall; Mrs Judith As-Seffar, Selly Oak Hospital, Birmingham; Mr Fred Roberts, Walsgrave Hospital, Coventry; Mr Melvyn Docker, Maternity Hospital, Queen Elizabeth Medical Centre, Birmingham; Miss Barbara Gill, Russell Hall Hospital, Dudley; Miss Sian Davies, Matthew Boulton College, Birmingham; Mrs Gillian Griffin; Mr Simon Redmore; Mrs Jenny Kelm.

Photographic material:
Frank Lane Picture Agency p.66
Science Photo Library p.70

The cover photograph shows a section of the spine and pelvic region as seen on X-ray. Also visible are the ureters draining from the kidneys to the bladder.

Printed in China

CONTENTS

General Editor's Introduction to the Series

Biology - Advanced Studies is a series of modular textbooks which are intended for students following advanced courses in biological subjects. The series offers the flexibility essential for working on modern syllabuses which often have core material and option topics. In particular, the books should be very useful for the new modular science courses which are emerging at A-Level.

In most of the titles in the series, one of the authors is a very experienced teacher (often also an examiner) and is sympathetic to the problems of learning at this level. The second author usually has research experience and is familiar with the subject at a higher level. In addition, several members of the writing team have been closely involved in the development of the latest syllabuses.

As with all text books, the reader may expect not to read from cover to cover but to study one topic at a time, or dip-in for information as needed. The index can be used like a science dictionary because where a page number is shown in bold print an explanation or definition will be found in the text. Where questions are asked, an attempt should be made at an answer because this type of *active reading* is the best way to develop an understanding of what is read.

We have referred throughout to *Biological nomenclature - Recommendations on terms, units and symbols*, Institute of Biology, London, 1989. We are delighted to be able to thank the many friends and colleagues who have helped with original ideas, the reading of drafts and the supply of illustrations.

Alan Cadogan
General Editor

Authors' Introduction to Human Systems

Biology courses at any level should be a worthwhile experience in their own right, while at the same time providing a preparation for subsequent studies or for possible employment. Syllabuses aim to develop an enjoyment in the study of organisms so that an interest and awareness of organisms and their inter-relationships can be developed. In this modern world it is also important that the student appreciates the development and significance of Biology in personal, social, environmental and technological contexts. These aspects of modern life are being stressed more and more in Advanced Biology syllabuses.

In earlier courses students should have been introduced to the important concepts and principles of Biology, gained knowledge about organisms and biological phenomena, and developed practical skills. In an Advanced course these objectives are considerably extended and developed The difference in the amount and depth of knowledge required to pass a lower level examination or to gain a good pass in Advanced Biology is considerable. The transition to the higher standard of knowledge cannot be made suddenly but should occupy the whole of a two year long course. Thus the process of learning, assimilating knowledge and gaining expertise can be likened to ascending a ramp over a period of time. Different students will ascend the ramp at different rates, according to their abilities, level of starting knowledge and application to hard work.

Physiology is a fascinating subject, however there are some difficulties for the student. This is because some of the concepts and mechanisms are complex, and because of the profusion of technical biological words that are required to describe the structures and physiological processes. In this book we have used and explained the terms you need to know.

The use of case studies in this book will, it is hoped, stimulate interest and illustrate some physiological points, whilst providing a personal, social and technological aspect to the physiological components of the Biology syllabuses. A number of questions are asked in the text and then answered at the end of the book. It is suggested that you first think about the question and then look up the answer.

The information in this textbook is what the authors, as experienced Chief Examiners and teachers, consider a good Advanced student should know about the Human Physiology components of their syllabuses after two years of study.

Martin Griffin and Alison Redmore

1

CELLS AND TISSUES

■ CASE STUDY: ABNORMAL CELL GROWTH

On her first visit to the local 'Well Woman Clinic' for several years, Mrs Jones looked smugly around the waiting room. At 39, she had never felt better in her life. She had managed to give up smoking, three months of aerobics classes had taken inches off her figure, and she and her family were just back from a relaxing holiday in sunny Spain. She certainly felt she was a 'well woman'!

The following month, she was more puzzled than worried when the clinic asked her to make an appointment to discuss the results of her routine cervical smear test. Despite feeling so well, it turned out that she had the early stages of cancer of the *cervix*. (The cervix is the entrance to the uterus.) It had taken only a few days for the results to come through; the technician in the hospital *cytology* department had stained a smear of her cervical cells and a number of cell abnormalities had been revealed. In many cells the nuclei were enlarged with irregular outlines, in some, the *chromatin* (genetic material) of the nuclei was coarse and unevenly distributed. In others, there were more nucleoli than there should be, and the cell cytoplasm often had vacuoles (membrane-bound spaces).

These changes are typical of cancerous (or *malignant*) cells. The good news was that no invasive 'tadpole-shaped' cells had been found, so the cancer was unlikely to have spread beyond the cervix. The bad news was that by now there were too many abnormal cells to treat them with lasers, so Mrs Jones had to have a hysterectomy (an operation to remove the womb). If only she had gone to the clinic earlier.

Q 1. The surfaces of the vagina and cervix shed cells more or less continuously, i.e. they exfoliate. (This is not be confused with the shedding of the lining of the uterus, the endometrium, during menstruation.) What other surfaces of the body do you think exfoliate cells continuously?

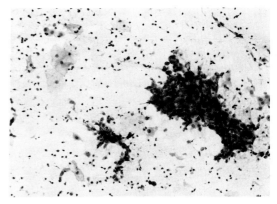

Photograph A

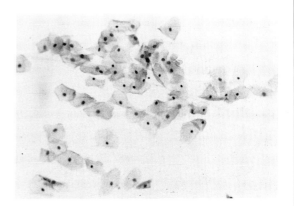

Photograph B

The photographs above show the cervical smears from two patients; one normal and one malignant.

2. Study photographs A and B above. Which do you think shows the normal cells, and which the malignant? Why?

3. Cancer cells eventually become migratory (the tadpole-shaped cells) and can invade other organs. Name some other body cells that can migrate under their own power.

■ LOOKING AT CELLS

Cells are the basic structural and functional units of all plants and animals. Every cell, whatever its function, has three parts which are responsible for forming the basic structure and performing the basic life functions of the cell. These three parts are: the *cell* (or *plasma*) *membrane* which maintains the cell's structure and controls the entry and exit of material; the *cytoplasm*, a semi-fluid medium where much of the cell's activities take place; and the *nucleus* which directs the cell's processes.

When cytologists look for abnormal cells, then obviously they must be very familiar with the appearance of normal cells of each type found in all of the body *tissues*. (A tissue is a group of similar cells performing a particular function. Tissues group together to form organs.)

The human egg cell is about the same size as the printed full stop at the end of this sentence. Most other cells are much smaller - in the range 7-20 micrometres (mm) in diameter. (A micrometre is a millionth of a metre, i.e. 10^{-6} metre.) A red blood cell (Fig.1.11) for example, is about 7.2 mm (i.e. 7.2×10^{-6}m) in diameter.

Biologists use the term *generalised cell* to describe the cell structures that are common to all cells, e.g. muscle cells, nerve cells and so on. Fig.1.1 is a drawing of a generalised animal cell to show the sort of detail that could be seen using a powerful light microscope (which would magnify it about 1000 times). It reveals the general shape of the cell, the cytoplasm and the nucleus. The nucleus is the largest *organelle* of the cell. (Organelles are small membrane-bound structures in the cytoplasm which have specific functions in the cell.) Within the nucleus can be seen a dark body, the *nucleolus*, a body containing RNA (ribose nucleic acid) and some chromatin material or DNA (deoxyribose nucleic acid). Granules, which are other organelles, can be seen in the cytoplasm, but their detailed structure cannot be seen under the light microscope. The largest of these granules are the mitochondria - the 'power plants' of the cell - where aerobic respiration takes place. Around the cytoplasm can be seen the plasma membrane.

The usefulness of the light microscope in discerning detail in cells and tissues can be enhanced by staining. Stains are used routinely to highlight parts of cells and tissues which otherwise are not clearly visible. Staining procedures often depend upon simple chemical reactions, such as between acids and bases. Particular stains are often specific to particular cell or tissue components, some structures attract acid stains and others attract basic stains. Some examples are shown in Table 1.1.

There is a much more powerful microscope that can reveal a wealth of detail about cell structure far beyond the limits of the light microscope. This is the electron microscope and it can magnify the image up to 500 000 times.

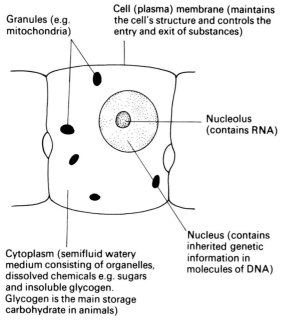

Granules (e.g. mitochondria)

Cell (plasma) membrane (maintains the cell's structure and controls the entry and exit of substances)

Nucleolus (contains RNA)

Nucleus (contains inherited genetic information in molecules of DNA)

Cytoplasm (semifluid watery medium consisting of organelles, dissolved chemicals e.g. sugars and insoluble glycogen. Glycogen is the main storage carbohydrate in animals)

Figure 1.1 Light microscope view of a stained generalised animal cell

Stain	Example	Type of cell structure	Example
Basic	Haematoxylin (blue)	Acidic components (basophilic or 'base-loving')	Chromatin (DNA), nucleoli (RNA), ribosomes (RNA)
Acidic	Eosin (red)	Basic components (acidophilic or 'acid-loving')	Cytoplasm, collagen

Table 1.1

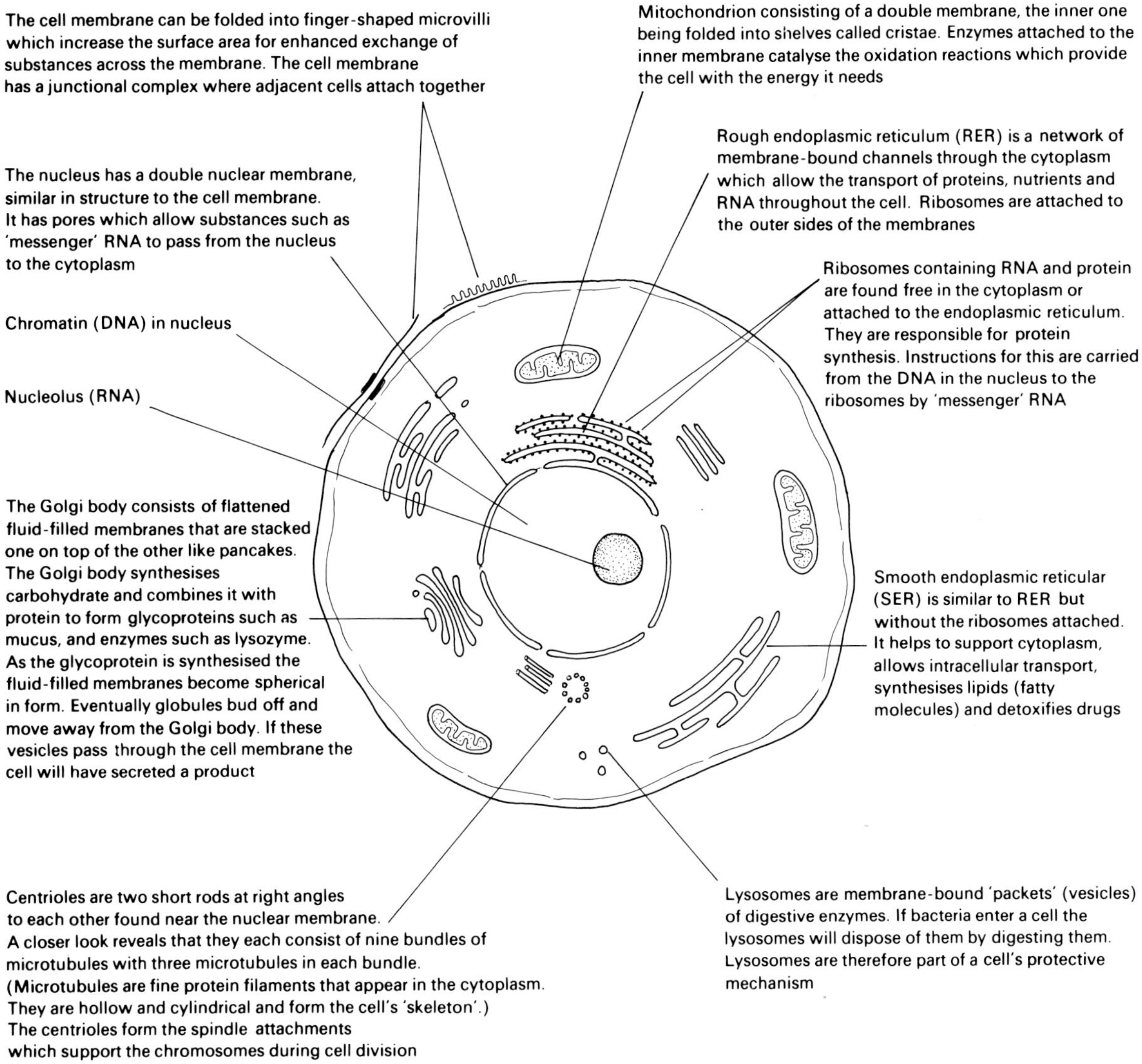

The cell membrane can be folded into finger-shaped microvilli which increase the surface area for enhanced exchange of substances across the membrane. The cell membrane has a junctional complex where adjacent cells attach together

Mitochondrion consisting of a double membrane, the inner one being folded into shelves called cristae. Enzymes attached to the inner membrane catalyse the oxidation reactions which provide the cell with the energy it needs

The nucleus has a double nuclear membrane, similar in structure to the cell membrane. It has pores which allow substances such as 'messenger' RNA to pass from the nucleus to the cytoplasm

Rough endoplasmic reticulum (RER) is a network of membrane-bound channels through the cytoplasm which allow the transport of proteins, nutrients and RNA throughout the cell. Ribosomes are attached to the outer sides of the membranes

Chromatin (DNA) in nucleus

Ribosomes containing RNA and protein are found free in the cytoplasm or attached to the endoplasmic reticulum. They are responsible for protein synthesis. Instructions for this are carried from the DNA in the nucleus to the ribosomes by 'messenger' RNA

Nucleolus (RNA)

The Golgi body consists of flattened fluid-filled membranes that are stacked one on top of the other like pancakes. The Golgi body synthesises carbohydrate and combines it with protein to form glycoproteins such as mucus, and enzymes such as lysozyme. As the glycoprotein is synthesised the fluid-filled membranes become spherical in form. Eventually globules bud off and move away from the Golgi body. If these vesicles pass through the cell membrane the cell will have secreted a product

Smooth endoplasmic reticular (SER) is similar to RER but without the ribosomes attached. It helps to support cytoplasm, allows intracellular transport, synthesises lipids (fatty molecules) and detoxifies drugs

Centrioles are two short rods at right angles to each other found near the nuclear membrane. A closer look reveals that they each consist of nine bundles of microtubules with three microtubules in each bundle. (Microtubules are fine protein filaments that appear in the cytoplasm. They are hollow and cylindrical and form the cell's 'skeleton'.) The centrioles form the spindle attachments which support the chromosomes during cell division

Lysosomes are membrane-bound 'packets' (vesicles) of digestive enzymes. If bacteria enter a cell the lysosomes will dispose of them by digesting them. Lysosomes are therefore part of a cell's protective mechanism

Figure 1.2 Electron microscope view of a generalised animal cell.

Carefully examine Fig.1.2 which is a drawing to show the detail of a generalised animal cell as seen under an electron microscope at moderate magnification. This detail is referred to as the *ultrastructure* of the cell.

In this book we are considering human systems, so it is important to understand how cells work together in tissues and organs. However, full details of cell ultrastructure and biochemistry are not required here. They will be found in other volumes of this series, namely, *Biology Advanced Studies - Biochemistry*, and *Biology Advanced Studies - Genetics and Evolution*.

The details of cell structure and ultrastructure described so far apply to almost all ***eukaryotic*** cells. However, cells do become specialised to perform certain tasks and thus the generalised features may become modified. Liver cells and nerve cells are commonly listed on the Advanced Level syllabuses as examples of specialised cells, and these will be considered now.

eukaryote a cell in which the nucleus is separated from the cytoplasm by a nuclear membrane. They are found in all organisms except bacteria and blue-green algae. These are prokaryotes and possess no nuclear membrane

■ Liver cell structure

Liver cells, or *hepatocytes* (Fig. 1.3) have a structure that adapts them for various functions. They are specialised cells because:

• they synthesise plasma proteins such as *albumin* and *fibrinogen* (an important substance for blood clotting). Thus, they have an extensive rough endoplasmic reticulum (rough ER) and a well developed Golgi body for synthesis and assembly of these substances.

• a number of cell metabolic processes occur at a fast rate so these metabolically active cells have numerous mitochondria to supply the necessary energy. For example, most of the fatty acid breakdown in the body happens in these cells.

• they store *glycogen* (produced from excess glucose - see Chapter 5) and fat. Thus the cells may contain numerous glycogen granules and fat droplets.

• they absorb many substances from the blood, such as glucose and amino acids, and pass others such as excretory urea, back into the blood. The area over which these exchanges are possible is increased because the cell's plasma membrane is extended into microvilli.

• the liver cells carry out the breakdown of poisons and drugs - detoxification - and have an extensive smooth ER to perform this function. Many of the breakdown products pass via microvilli into the bile, e.g. bile pigments which are made during the breakdown of haemoglobin when old red blood cells are destroyed. Bile drains into the gall bladder where it is stored until it is added to the food in the duodenum. So these breakdown products eventually pass out of the body with the faeces. (The location of the liver and gall bladder can be seen in Fig. 6.1.)

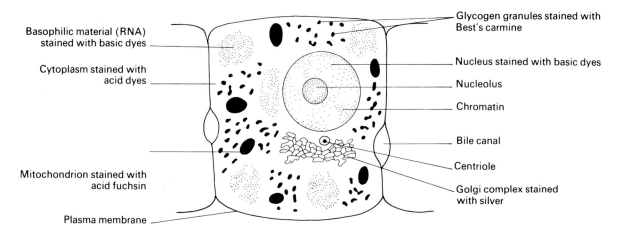

Figure 1.3 (a) A stained liver cell (light microscope view). The original slide was made using a variety of stains, each of which is picked up by different cell organelles

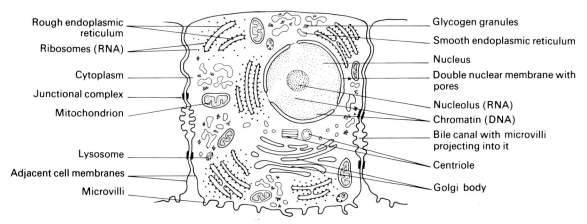

Figure 1.3 (b) A stained liver cell (electron microscope view). More detailed structures are visible. This helps us to understand how the cell organelles function

■ Neurone cell structure

Carefully examine Figs.1.4(a) and (b). Nerve cells (*neurones*) are adapted for transmitting nerve impulses over long distances. Each neurone has:
• a cell body which houses the nucleus and a long fibre or (*axon*) which conducts the impulses to their destination. (You should refer to Chapter 7 for further details of the 'working neurones'.)

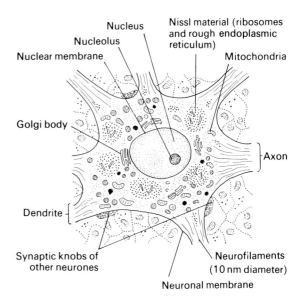

Figure 1.4 (b) Motor neurone (electron microscope view). This shows the structure of the cell body in more detail

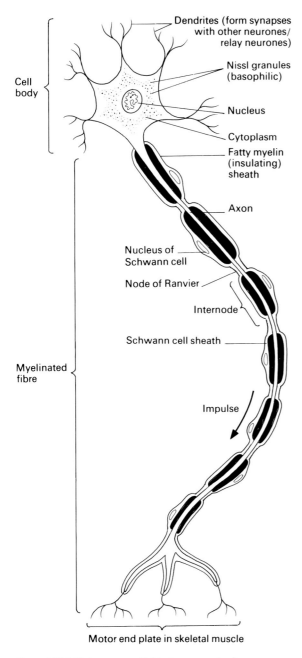

Figure 1.4 (a) Motor neurone (light microscope view)

• a fatty layer, the *myelin sheath*, around the axon which insulates one fibre from all of the others. The sheath, which is produced by separate *Schwann cells* is interrupted at points called the *nodes of Ranvier*. These cause nerve impulses to 'jump' from node to node giving a faster rate of impulse conduction than would happen without these nodes. The speed of transmission along axons can be 60ms^{-1}.
• fine extension processes to the cell body called dendrons which branch into numerous *dendrites*. These give the cell a large surface area to link with other neurones, i.e. to **synapse**.
• an axon which is also branched at its end to increase the surface area for making synapses. The end branches have *synaptic knobs* (*boutons*) where there are cell vesicles which make and release the chemicals needed to transmit the nerve impulse over the synapse gap. The most common transmitter substance is *acetylcholine*.
• numerous mitochondria throughout the neurone which provide the energy required for acetylcholine synthesis and for maintaining the *sodium and potassium pumps* needed for nerve impulse transmission (see Fig.7.2(a) for details).
• cytoplasm (called *axoplasm*) streaming between the cell body and the fibre in both directions. There

---

synapse a gap of about 20 nm between neurones. It is bridged by transmitter chemicals at the time of impulse conduction (also used as a verb - to synapse)

are fine *microtubules* and *microfilaments* (made of the protein actin) running through the cytoplasm along the axon. These may well help to direct the streaming of cytoplasm and organelles and carry out transport inside the cell. They also help to maintain the cell shape by acting as a *cytoskeleton*.

• many organelles called *Nissl granules* in the cell bodies. These granules contain mitochondria, free ribosomes and short lengths of rough ER. They are concerned with protein synthesis, probably of enzymes involved in nerve impulse transmission, and with the synthesis of *trophic factors* which regulate the growth and development of nervous tissue.

Q 4. What type of cell division is involved when liver cells divide to form new liver cells or when new neurones are formed?

■ DIFFERENTIATION AND AGGREGATION OF CELLS INTO TISSUES

From a functional point of view there would be little point in having single liver or neurone cells. Large numbers of each type cluster together and have a common function. This is the meaning of the term *tissue*. The structure of the outer surface of cells is very important when cells meet and cluster together. The surface of one cell must recognise and accept the surfaces of other similar cells and they must remain in various degrees of contact to hold the tissues together. The outer surface of the cell is its plasma membrane which has a coat (*glycocalyx*) of molecules of complex branching carbohydrate chains. This appears to be involved in cell recognition by either allowing or preventing contact between plasma membranes of adjacent cells. The ultrastructure of the plasma membrane can be seen in Fig.1.5. Note the glycocalyx on the outside of the membrane and the extrinsic and intrinsic proteins.

The cell membrane also has *receptor sites* on its outer surface, probably on the protein components. These allow local recognition and aggregation when cells with similar receptor sites come into contact. What happens when nerve cells come into contact with each other is particularly interesting. A neurone secretes *trophic factors* which affect nearby cells in three main ways. Firstly, these substances establish and maintain contact between the two neurones at a synapse and between a nerve fibre and a muscle at

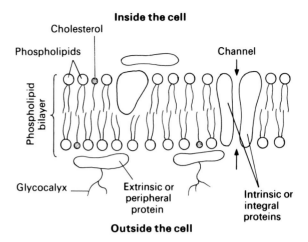

Figure 1.5 A model of the ultrastructure of the cell membrane showing the position of different molecules

neuromuscular junctions (Fig.1.4). Secondly, they cause the plasma membrane of the neurone following the synapse, (i.e. the *post-synaptic membrane*,) to develop receptors for specific transmitter substances such as acetylcholine or noradrenaline. Thirdly, the trophic factors are transmitted back up the axon body to 'inform' the cell about what type of surface the fibre is in contact with at its other end, so that appropriate synapses can be developed. Within the nervous system new synapses are continually being formed while others break up. Trophic factors help to make this an organised process, so that only specific links are made between neurones.

■ Adhesion
When cells of the same type come into contact, they are held together by a *junctional complex* (Fig.1.3(b)) which consists of three types of adhesion. A good example of cells being held closely together is in the layers of surface cells (*epithelial cells*) which must form good strong covering tissue.

The three types of adhesion at a complex are:
• where the membranes of neighbouring cells seem to fuse together in places with no space between them (*tight junctions*). This means that the exchange of substances between cells can be controlled.
• where the membranes between the cells are separated by a gap of about 20 nm but with many fine filaments crossing the gap and strengthening the connection. This is an *intermediate junction*.
• where *desmosomes* occur. These are like minute spot-welds between the membranes of adjacent

cells. From the dense material of the desmosome, fine microfilaments run into the cytoplasm on both sides, fusing with the microtubules of the two cells.

The junctional complex serves, not only to hold cells together, but also to share out stresses (such as the stretching of skin) between a number of cells. They also control the diffusion of chemicals between cells. The adhesions can become unstuck, for example, wound healing occurs only because cells from areas around the wound can become detached from the tissue and move to form a skin to cover the wound. Returning to the case of Mrs Jones (see page 1), some cancer cells also lose the power to adhere to other cells in the tissue. They move away becoming invasive and colonise areas between the cells of other tissues. Here they can multiply forming new growths (secondaries).

■ Differentiation

This literally means 'becoming different' and refers to the changes in the structure and function of a cell as it develops from a general unspecialised cell to one of the specialised types. Cell differentiation is controlled genetically. The first cell of the organism, the *zygote* has a complete *genetic blueprint*, made up of genetic material received from both parents. Since further growth occurs by cell division (*mitosis*) every somatic, or body cell of the organism will contain the same genetic blueprint, identical to that of the zygote (see Chapter 8). The cells develop differently to give the many types found in tissues and organs of the body. Different cells must therefore be using different parts of the blueprint; some genes must be 'switched on' and others 'switched off' to produce the special characteristics of the cell type.

Gene action is complex but in the 1950s Jacob and Monod were able to show a link between some *structural genes* (which govern the amino acid sequences of structural proteins and enzymes) and *regulator genes* (which control the activity of the structural genes). They used the term *operon* for this system of linked genes, and demonstrated that operons could be influenced by chemical or physical changes. For example, operons in the intestinal bacterium, *Escherichia coli*, will switch on to produce lactose-splitting enzymes only if lactose is present in the intestines. Other operons for enzyme production are switched on or off in liver cells depending on the levels of nutrients arriving there from the intestine.

Some operons have an effect at certain stages of development. For instance, fetal haemoglobin is different from the haemoglobin produced after birth in that it has a higher oxygen affinity. Thus it can collect oxygen from the mother's haemoglobin across the **placenta**. At birth the operon for causing the manufacture of fetal haemoglobin is turned off, while the operon for making adult haemoglobin is switched on.

It is now known that a number of factors can cause abnormaility in the fetus. Chemicals (*teratogens*) which cause genetic damage are able to pass through the placental barrier and damage active genes or switch on unwanted ones at an important stage of fetus development. Most people are familiar with the teratogenic effects of some industrial chemicals, some pesticides, drugs (such as thalidomide and LSD) and ionising radiation. Large doses of X-rays received in early pregnancy may cause microcephaly (small head), mental retardation and malformation of the skeleton. Fig.1.6 shows a child with a hare lip, an example of fetal damage caused by teratogens.

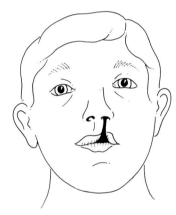

Figure 1.6 Child with a harelip

The main point to remember about differentiation is that all cells have the potential to be the same as they all have the same genes. We believe that cells become different because of their environment - this includes not only the chemical and physical factors, but also the effect of the cytoplasm cell which is derived from the female parent (the egg cell cytoplasm).

> **placenta** the 'life-support system' of the fetus, where the mother's blood and fetal blood come very close together (but do not mix). Thus exchange of gases, nutrients and waste materials can take place between the two blood systems

Q 5. Doctors advise that children (and particularly girls) should be immunised against rubella (German measles). Do you know the reason for this advice?

■ HISTOLOGY

Histology is the study of tissues, the word being derived from two Greek words, *histos* meaning a tissue, and *logos* meaning a study of. In the body there are four major classes of tissues:

• *Epithelial tissues*. These have the overall function of covering surfaces thus providing protection, but also are developed to form secretory (glandular) tissues.

• *Connective tissues*. These join the body together and make up much of the 'structural' material of the body.

• *Muscular tissues*. These allow for all movements, such as walking, heart beating or stomach churning.

• *Nervous tissues*. These enable the body to work in a co-ordinated manner, and allow responses to changes in the environment.

Within these major classes are a number of specialised types of tissue (Fig.1.7). Remember that all the specialised tissue types originated from undifferentiated cells.

The epithelial tissues and blood will be dealt with in this chapter as an introduction to histology and to demonstrate the close relationships between structure, function and physiological mechanisms. The histology of the remaining tissues are described in subsequent chapters.

■ The histology and functions of epithelia

Epithelia form the outer coverings of organs and body structures, and the lining of the insides of tubes and hollow organs. Epithelia are protective but they have other specialised functions in particular situations. For example, skin is a complex epithelium adapted to form a barrier with the external environment; the bladder is lined with another type of epithelium which is adapted to withstand the toxic chemicals of the urine. Most of the glands of the body are derived from specialised epithelial tissue.

Covering epithelia are of two main types. In *simple epithelia* all the cells touch a basement membrane, and in *compound epithelia* only the lower layer of cells touches the basement membrane. The basement membrane in all cases is made of fine fibres of *collagen*.

The range of epithelial types can be seen in Fig.1.8.

■ Squamous (pavement) epithelium

Squamous epithelium (Fig.1.8(a)) is very common and is found in many parts of the body. The cells are often described as being like 'crazy paving' slabs in surface view and like flattened blocks in side view (vertical section). The nuclei are disc-shaped. Squamous epithelium lines the body cavities and continues over the outer surface of the *viscera* (internal organs). It also lines the inner surfaces of blood vessels and the heart chambers.

In the squamous epithelium of the capillaries there are small windows (fenestrations) between the epithelial cells. These make the capillaries

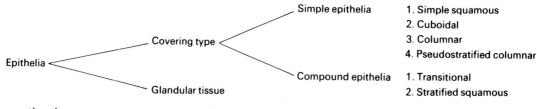

Figure 1.7 Tissue types

Simple epithelia
1. Simple squamous
2. Cuboidal
3. Columnar
4. Pseudostratified columnar

Covering type

Epithelia

Glandular tissue

Compound epithelia
1. Transitional
2. Stratified squamous

Connective tissue
1. Blood
2. Areolar connective tissue
3. White fibrous tissue
4. Yellow elastic tissue
5. Cartilage
6. Bone

Muscular tissue
1. Smooth muscle
2. Striated muscle
3. Cardiac (heart) muscle

Nervous tissue
1. Neurones
2. Receptors
3. Neuroglial cells (supporting tissue)

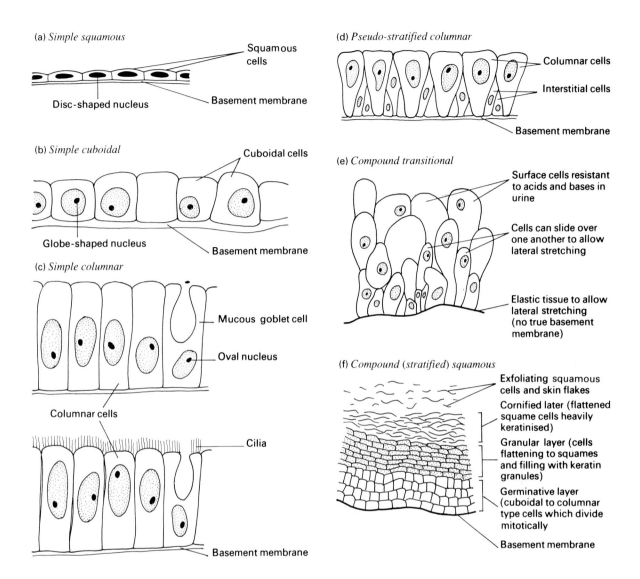

(a) *Simple squamous*

Squamous cells

Disc-shaped nucleus

Basement membrane

(b) *Simple cuboidal*

Cuboidal cells

Globe-shaped nucleus

Basement membrane

(c) *Simple columnar*

Mucous goblet cell

Oval nucleus

Columnar cells

Cilia

Basement membrane

(d) *Pseudo-stratified columnar*

Columnar cells

Interstitial cells

Basement membrane

(e) *Compound transitional*

Surface cells resistant to acids and bases in urine

Cells can slide over one another to allow lateral stretching

Elastic tissue to allow lateral stretching (no true basement membrane)

(f) *Compound (stratified) squamous*

Exfoliating squamous cells and skin flakes

Cornified later (flattened squame cells heavily keratinised)

Granular layer (cells flattening to squames and filling with keratin granules)

Germinative layer (cuboidal to columnar type cells which divide mitotically

Basement membrane

Figure 1.8 Types of epithelia (in vertical section): **(a)** simple squamous epithelium, **(b)** simple cuboidal epithelium, **(c)** simple columnar epithelium, **(d)** pseudostratified columnar epithelium, **(e)** compound transitional epithelium of the bladder, **(f)** compound (stratified) squamous epithelium of the epidermis (nuclei omitted)

'leaky' and improve the exchange of substances between the blood and the tissues. Certain white corpuscles are able to squeeze out through these gaps - a process known as *diapedesis*.

In the blood spaces known as *sinusoids*, found in the liver, spleen, thymus and lymph nodes, some epithelial cells are modified into *phagocytes* (*fixed macrophages*). These are cells which can engulf cell debris and bacteria in a process known as *phagocytosis*. In the epithelium of the lung alveoli, fixed macrophages (called dust cells) engulf dust particles from the air. Other cells nearby secrete *surfactants* which lubricate the surfaces and allow the lungs to change size during ventilation. The thinness of this epithelium in the alveoli enhances gaseous exchange.

Modified squamous cells are found in the kidney.

Cuboidal epithelium

Cuboidal: epithelium (Fig.1.8(b)) consists of cube-shaped cells and is found covering the surface of the ovary, and lining a number of structures such as the kidney nephron tubules, the thyroid follicles, the smallest bronchioles of the lung, and the interlobular bile ducts of the liver (Fig.6.5). Some cells, such as those in the nephrons and thyroid have microvilli, which allow enhanced exchange across the cell membranes. In the kidney nephrons this is important for efficient urine formation, and in the thyroid they allow adequate absorption of iodine into the follicles, and efficient release of *hormones* from the follicles into the blood.

 6. There is a layer of cuboidal epithelium behind the retina in the eye in which the cells contain the black pigment, melanin. What is the function of this layer?

Columnar epithelium

In columnar epithelium (Fig.1.8(c)) the cells form rectangular pillars, with oval nuclei towards the base of the cells. Depending on its location in the body columnar epithelium may be modified to become *mucous, ciliated* or *absorptive*. Mucous epithelia have *goblet cells* which secrete *mucin*, a glycoprotein, which when mixed with water on the surface of the cell forms *mucus*. This lubricates and protects the surface of the epithelium.

Mucous columnar epithelium lines the inside of the digestive tract from the stomach up to the posterior third of the rectum. The mucus lubricates the food passing through and reduces the risk of the gut lining being ulcerated by the digestive enzymes, acids and alkalis. Mucous columnar epithelium is also found lining the inside of the gall bladder and the larger bronchioles in the lungs.

Ciliated epithelial cells are found with mucous cells and have millions of fine threads or cilia, which beat synchronously within the layer of mucus setting up a current. They line the smaller bronchi of the lungs, the oviducts and the uterus, the central canal of the spinal cord, and the spaces (*ventricles*) within the brain.

 7. What functions do you think the cilia have in: (a) the bronchi, and (b) the oviducts?

Absorptive columnar cells with microvilli line the small intestine, so increasing the surface area for absorption of the products of digestion.

Pseudostratified columnar epithelium

At first glance, the pseudostratified columnar epithelium (Fig.1.8(d)) appears to consist of several layers of cells. Careful inspection however, will show that each cell is fixed to the basement membrane, although not all of them reach the surface. The epithelium is ciliated, and usually contains mucous goblet cells. It is found lining the vas deferens, and the upper respiratory tract (trachea and *nasal mucosa*).

Transitional epithelium

Transitional epithelium (Fig.1.8(e)) is a compound epithelium between two and seven cells thick, as the cells can slide over one another sideways. It is found in the ureter and bladder where it allows for expansion as the bladder fills with urine. The outer surface of the top layer of transitional cells is thick and fairly rigid. This is probably waterporoof so that osmotic exchange cannot occur with the urine.

Stratified squamous epithelium

Stratified squamous epithelium (Fig.1.8(f)) makes up the epidermis of the skin (page 11), and also lines the mouth (*buccal*) and nasal cavities, the urethra, vagina and final third of the rectum. It has many layers of cells, which are constantly being renewed from the base and exfoliating (being shed) from the surface. The basal cells divide by *mitosis* to form new cuboidal or columnar cells, pushing older cells up towards the surface to thicken the epithelium. The outer layers contain flattened, squamous cells, and it is these that flake off. The outer squamous cells are dead because cells die as they are pushed beyond the limits for exchange by diffusion with the blood capillaries on the other side of the basement membrane.

Glands

During development, some epithelial tissue gives rise to glandular tissue by becoming folded into various three dimensional arrangements. Fig.1.9 illustrates some of these.

A single mucous goblet cell could be considered as a unicellular gland, although the term gland is usually applied to many secretory cells grouped together. *Exocrine glands* are glands that release their secretions through ducts onto a surface or into a cavity of the body. The secretory cells of exocrine glands are commonly arranged either in tubular form or as flask-shaped (*acinar*) glands, or as combinations of the two.

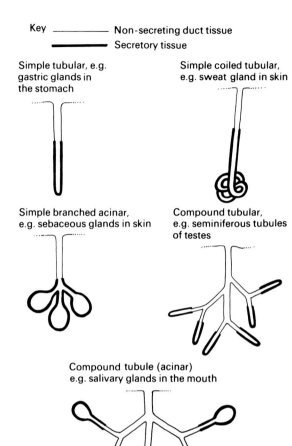

Key ———————— Non-secreting duct tissue
▬▬▬▬▬▬ Secretory tissue

Simple tubular, e.g. gastric glands in the stomach

Simple coiled tubular, e.g. sweat gland in skin

Simple branched acinar, e.g. sebaceous glands in skin

Compound tubular, e.g. seminiferous tubules of testes

Compound tubule (acinar) e.g. salivary glands in the mouth

Figure 1.9 Histological arrangement of exocrine glands . (Note that in an endocrine gland the duct system is lost and the secretion is emptied into a profuse blood system.)

Tubular glands may be *simple*, such as the fundic glands of the stomach which secrete gastric juice, and the crypts of Lieberkuhn in the duodenum; or *coiled*, e.g. sweat glands. Acinar glands include the salivary glands and the sebaceous glands which produce the oily secretion in the hair follicles.

Some glandular tissue has developed so that the connecting duct between the secretory tissue and the surface is absent. These glands are termed *endocrine* (ductless) glands and they empty their secretions (hormones) directly into the bloodstream. (These glands are considered at length in Chapter 7.)

■ Cells to tissues to organs

The grouping together of cells into epithelia is an example of the tissue level of organisation. Epithelial tissue generally contains cells of the same type doing the same job - however, some tissues can contain cells of several types (an example is, blood which is a connective tissue). Other tissues, such as tendons, contain fibres as well as cells.

When different tissues are themselves aggregated together to perform a function they form structures known as *organs*, e.g. the skin, the stomach and the heart. Of course, the heart is only one organ in the circulation system; and the stomach, one organ in the digestive system. All of the organs work together in an organism. So, we can now say that the main *levels of organisation* in the human body are: cells - tissues - organs - organ systems - organism. (We could go to other levels, the *sub-cellular* and *molecular* at one extreme and the *population*, *community* and *ecosystem* at the other extreme, but these levels are the subject matter of other books in this series!)

■ STRUCTURE AND FUNCTIONS OF THE SKIN

The structure of the skin (in vertical sections) can be seen in Fig.1.10.

The skin is interesting because it is the largest organ of the body. It is the interface of the organism with the environment and it has several important functions:
• it receives sensory stimuli letting the organism know what is happening around it.
• it protects the body from water loss and from becoming waterlogged.
• it prevents the entry of bacteria and other pathogens.
• it can stretch to enable movement.

The outermost layer of skin is a stratified squamous epithelium called the *epidermis*. At the base of the epithelium is a layer of cells (the *germinative* or *malpighian layer*) which divide constantly by mitosis. The older skin cells die and become impregnated with a fibrous protein, *alpha-keratin*. This helps to harden the skin and make it waterproof. Waterproofing is also aided by the secretion of *sebum* from the sebaceous glands.

The skin exfoliates from its surface as the outer dead cells flake off. Thus friction is unlikely to wear away any living tissue, since the dead cells are shed with so little resistance.

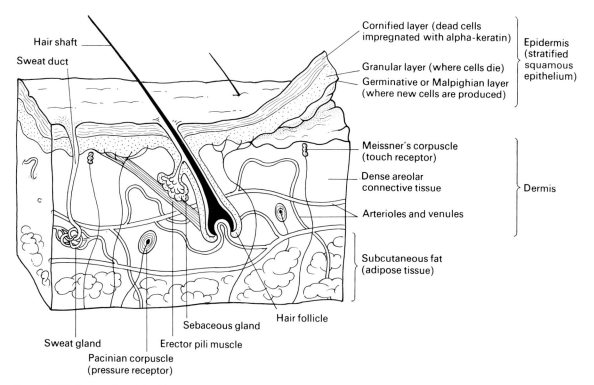

Hair shaft

Sweat duct

Cornified layer (dead cells
impregnated with alpha-keratin)

Granular layer (where cells die)

Germinative or Malpighian layer
(where new cells are produced)

Epidermis
(stratified
squamous
epithelium)

Meissner's corpuscle
(touch receptor)

Dense areolar
connective tissue

Arterioles and venules

Dermis

Subcutaneous fat
(adipose tissue)

Hair follicle

Sebaceous gland

Sweat gland

Erector pili muscle

Pacinian corpuscle
(pressure receptor)

Figure 1.10 Vertical section of the skin

As well as maintaining the thickness of the skin, the cells of the malpighian layer also produce *melanin*, a brown or black pigment that absorbs the harmful ultraviolet rays from sunlight.

The epidermis covering different parts of the body may be modified to form hairs and sweat glands, both of which are important in temperature regulation (pages 79 and 80).

Beneath the epidermis lies the dermis, the inner layer of the skin. This is composed of areolar connective tissue (see Chapter 2) which gives the skin its elasticity, allowing it to stretch and be pulled while still maintaining its undamaged structure. The dermis also contains fat store cells (adipose tissue) for insulation; an extensive capillary network; and receptor nerve cells sensitive to touch, pressure, pain and temperature. The sweat glands and hair follicles, although derived from the epidermis, actually appear in the dermal layer.

 8. What is sunburn and why does sunburnt skin usually peel?

9. Suggest how the epidermis on the soles of your feet is able to become so much thicker than elsewhere on your body.

10. A severe burn may destroy quite a large area of epidermis. Why is this dangerous?

■ THE STRUCTURE AND FUNCTIONS OF BLOOD

The functions of blood are mainly related to transport and defence, although it is also responsible for forming the intercellular fluid, so it is important in **homeostasis**. Substances that are transported by blood include respiratory gases, food substances, excretory products, hormones, cells and antibodies. The defensive functions of blood involve phagocytosis, the immune response, and clotting (*haemostasis*).

About 55% of the blood volume consists of a straw-coloured aqueous solution called plasma, the other 45% being occupied by cells. The cells (corpuscles) are either red (*erythrocytes*) or white (*leucocytes*) though there are also fragments of cytoplasm present, called platelets (*thrombocytes*).

---

homeostasis the maintenance of the internal environment (inside of the organism) within narrow controlled limits

---

Cell type	Size (m)	Life span	Function
Erythrocyte	7.7	120 days	Transport of respiratory gases
Leucocytes (five types)	7 to 19	Few days to few hours	Various defence functions
Thrombocyte	2 to 4	5 to 9 days	Clotting

Table 1.2 Characteristics of different blood cells

The erythrocytes are the most abundant cells, with about five million of them in every cubic millimetre of blood, compared with about quarter of a million thrombocytes, and only 5000 to 9000 leucocytes in the same volume. Table 1.2 summarises the cell types, sizes, life span and functions, and Fig.1.9 shows their structure.

■ Blood plasma

The composition of plasma is closely regulated by the kidneys, so that its osmotic pressure, pH, salt concentration, and the concentrations of many of its other constituents, remain within the strict limits of what is the most suitable (*optimum*) environment for the cells. Plasma contains a number of plasma proteins, the main groups being albumins, globulins, and clotting factors such as fibrinogen. Albumins and fibrinogen are made by the liver and secreted into the blood, while the gamma globulins, which are antibodies, are secreted by plasma cells already present in the blood and lymphatic systems (page 18). Albumins are the most abundant of the plasma proteins and are responsible for much of the osmotic pressure of blood. This osmotic pressure helps to hold water in the blood, so maintaining blood volume and pressure. Albumins and some globulins may also act as carrier proteins for substances that are insoluble in the watery plasma. Thyroxine, for example, is transported from the thyroid gland by attaching onto a specific globulin, while cholesterol is carried on lipoproteins - molecules made up of fat plus protein units.

■ Erythrocyte structure

Erythrocytes (Fig.1.12(a)) are little more than packets of the protein, *haemoglobin*, surrounded by a cell membrane. The nucleus is lost during differentiation in the red bone marrow, and a mature red cell is shaped like a *biconcave disc*. The disc shape gives it a large surface area in relation to volume, as required for efficient gas exchange. The shape can also be distorted to allow cells to

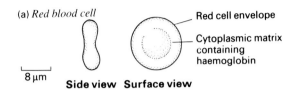

(a) *Red blood cell*

Red cell envelope

Cytoplasmic matrix containing haemoglobin

8 μm

Side view   Surface view

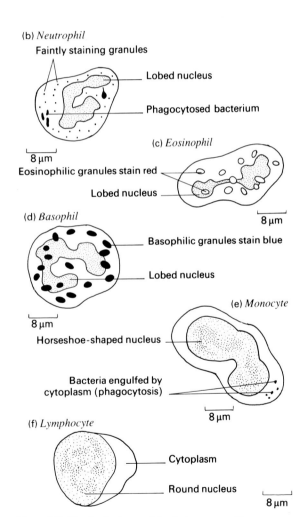

(b) *Neutrophil*
Faintly staining granules

Lobed nucleus

Phagocytosed bacterium

8 μm

(c) *Eosinophil*

Eosinophilic granules stain red

Lobed nucleus

8 μm

(d) *Basophil*

Basophilic granules stain blue

Lobed nucleus

8 μm

Horseshoe-shaped nucleus

(e) *Monocyte*

Bacteria engulfed by cytoplasm (phagocytosis)

8 μm

(f) *Lymphocyte*

Cytoplasm

Round nucleus

8 μm

Figure 1.11 Blood cells from a stained microscope slide (drawn to scale): (a) red blood cell, and white blood cells; (b) neutrophil, (c) eosinophil, (d) basophil, (e) monocyte, (f) lymphocyte

squeeze through narrow sinusoids (irregular spaces) and capillaries as narrow as six micrometres in diameter. The passage of red cells through capillaries is slowed up by this, allowing even greater efficiency in gas exchange. Erythrocytes normally stay in the blood stream.

 11. What is the diameter of a red blood cell?

■ THE ROLE OF HAEMOGLOBIN

■ Transport of oxygen

The respiratory pigment, *haemoglobin*, allows blood to carry enough oxygen for the body's needs. The solubility of oxygen in the water of the plasma is really very low, and decreases even further as the temperature rises. So the amount of oxygen that could be carried dissolved in plasma alone would not be enough. The extra loading of oxygen depends on the fact that one molecule of haemoglobin can 'on-load' four molecules of oxygen - one on each of the iron atoms in the molecule.

Inhaled alveolar air is described as having an oxygen tension of 14 kPa (kilopascals) whereas the oxygen tension in the blood supplying the lungs is between 2.7 kPa and 5.3 kPa. (The range depends on the oxygen tension of the tissues the blood has just left; 2.7 kPa for active tissues like working muscles and 5.3 kPa for tissues of resting cells.) This means that there will be a difference or *diffusion gradient* across the respiratory surface (e.g. 14 kPa – 5.3 kPa = 8.7 kPa) and so the oxygen will pass from the alveoli into the blood, and into the red blood cells. Once in the red blood cells, the oxygen is 'on-loaded' until the haemoglobin is about 97% saturated. *Oxyhaemoglobin* is formed.

It can be seen from Fig.1.12 that the middle curve (normal blood at pH 7.4) shows that at low levels of oxygen, only a small percentage of the haemoglobin is saturated with oxygen. As the 'oxygen pressure' (oxygen tension is the correct term!) increases, there is a steep increase in the percentage saturation of the haemoglobin. In fact, at 14 kPa the haemoglobin is unable to combine with any more oxygen and is said to be 100% saturated. That is the situation when blood flows through the capillaries of the lung alveoli and the red blood cells on-load oxygen. When this oxygenated blood reaches resting cells (basal metabolic rate) it off-loads its oxygen.

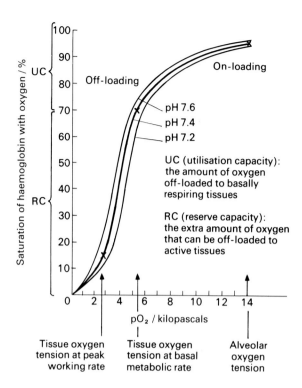

Figure 1.12 Oxygen-haemoglobin association-dissociation curves. The equation for *association* is given as: $Hb + 4O_2 \rightarrow HbO_8$. The equation for *dissociation* is given as:
$HbO_8 \rightarrow HbO_6 \rightarrow HbO_4 \rightarrow HbO_2 \rightarrow Hb$, where Hb represents the whole molecule of haemoglobin

 12. Using Fig.1.12, work out the percentage of oxygen off-loaded by oxygenated blood when it reaches resting cells.

Active respiring tissues use up more oxygen so the surrounding oxygen tension is reduced to the range of 2.7 to 5.3 kPa. When the red blood cells reach this area, oxyhaemoglobin releases its oxygen (i.e. dissociates) and off-loads its oxygen to the surrounding tissues.

The amount of oxygen carried by haemoglobin depends on pH as well as on oxygen tension. In a more acid environment (pH 7.2) oxygen dissociates from the haemoglobin more readily, whilst more alkaline conditions (pH 7.6) favour association and the formation of oxyhaemoglobin. This results in the *Bohr effect* which is illustrated in Fig.1.12. (Remember that the pH scale is measured at 25 °C when pH 7 is neutral. At body temperature, 37 °C, the neutral pH value is slightly higher.)

Respiring tissues produce an *acidic environment* in the blood capillaries, owing to a high concentration of lactic acid from muscle metabolism and a high carbon dioxide tension from cell respiration. Hydrogen ions can reduce haemoglobin by attaching to the same sites as the oxygen atoms, and they therefore compete with oxygen for those sites. In an acidic pH the higher concentration of hydrogen ions displaces oxygen from haemoglobin, and so improves the efficiency of oxygen release into the tissues. In the less acidic environment of the alveoli, oxygen atoms predominate and so tend to displace the hydrogen ions from haemoglobin, thus enhancing the uptake of oxygen. In this way, haemoglobin acts in the blood as a buffer, preventing large changes in pH. This is another example of homeostasis - in this case keeping the pH at an optimum level.

■ Transport of carbon dioxide

Carbon dioxide is released from respiring cells and diffuses into the plasma. Only 5% of it dissolves directly and is carried in solution. Most diffuses into the erythrocytes and about 25% links up to the protein part of haemoglobin to form *carbaminohaemoglobin*. (The haemoglobin is still able to carry oxygen or hydrogen on its haem groups.) The remaining 70% of the carbon dioxide is converted by the red blood cell enzyme, carbonic anhydrase, to carbonic acid. This immediately dissociates into hydrogen ions and hydrogencarbonate ions, via carbonic acid:

$$CO_2 + H_2O \xrightarrow{\text{Carbonic anhydrase}} H_2CO_3 \xrightarrow{\hspace{1cm}} H^+ + HCO_3$$

(Carbonic Acid)

The hydrogen ions would decrease the pH of the blood if they remained free. Instead, they attach to the haem groups displacing and forcing out the oxygen into the tissues, so the pH falls no lower than pH 7.2. The hydrogen carbonate ions diffuse out of the red blood cells into the plasma. This leaves a shortage of negative ions in the red blood cells. Chloride (Cl^-) ions move from the plasma into the red blood cells to restore the balance. This is known as the *chloride shift*.

At the alveoli, the equilibria of these reactions is reversed. Carbaminohaemoglobin releases its carbon dioxide into the alveoli, and the high oxygen tension dislodges the hydrogen ions from the haem groups. Hydrogen ions react more easily with hydrogencarbonate than with chloride, so hydrogencarbonate ions diffuse back into the red

blood cell in exchange for chloride ions. Carbonic acid reforms, and then dissociates under the influence of carbonic anhydrase to give water and carbon dioxide. This diffuses down the concentration gradient into the alveolar air and is expired. The pH rises no higher than pH 7.6. (Now you can see why in Fig.1.12 there are three curves; one for pH 7.2 another for pH 7.6, and a third for the normal blood pH 7.4.) Do not confuse carbamino-haemoglobin with *carboxyhaemoglobin*. The latter forms when *carbon monoxide* attaches strongly to the haem sites instead of oxygen. This effectively poisons the haemoglobin molecule and so reduces the oxygen-carrying capacity of the blood. Carbon monoxide poisoning can result in death.

 13. Fetal haemoglobin has to collect oxygen from maternal haemoglobin across the placenta. Will fetal haemoglobin have a greater or smaller affinity for oxygen than maternal haemoglobin in low oxygen tensions?

14. Where would the association/dissociation curve of fetal haemoglobin lie on the graph shown in Fig.1.12?

■ Formation of new red blood cells (erythropoiesis)

Red blood cells are formed in the red bone marrow, and have an average life span in the circulation of about 120 days. A continual supply of iron is required to synthesise the haemoglobin; and vitamin B_{12} and folic acid must also be present. The rate at which red blood cells are formed is under hormonal control and is stimulated by *anoxia* (a lack of oxygen reaching the tissues).

15. Suggest three factors which could cause a deficiency of oxygen at tissue level.

Hypoxia acts on the kidneys causing them to release an enzyme (renin) into the blood which catalyses the breakdown of a plasma globulin. One breakdown product is a hormone called *erythropoietin* which speeds up red blood cell formation in the red bone marrow by increasing the rate of mitosis there.

Fetal red blood cells are made in the liver. After birth the liver is concerned with breaking down aged red blood cells. In adults, red cell formation takes place only in the red bone marrow. This is found in the sternum, ribs, vertebrae, pelvic girdle and long bones.

Vitamin B_{12} catalyses an essential step in DNA formation and cell division. It is absorbed from the ileum, provided it has been protected from stomach enzymes by first reacting with a substance called *intrinsic factor*. This factor is present in normal gastric juice, but if it is absent vitamin B_{12} is destroyed rather than absorbed, and once the liver's store of the vitamin has been used up *pernicious anaemia* results.

Lack of folic acid inhibits mitosis and thus lowers the rate of red blood cell production. It also has an interesting effect in that it helps the change of uracil, a base in the RNA molecule, to thymine, a base in the DNA molecule. This is important in the chemistry of protein synthesis in the cell.

■ CASE STUDY: A LINK BETWEEN DIET AND HEALTH

Mr William Brown had always been fond of cream buns. He had also always been overweight, but his doctor had finally persuaded him that at 56 years of age he must lose weight or risk a coronary. The dietitian gave him a 'sensible' diet, which William promptly threw in the bin. He decided to cut out the things he enjoyed the least, like meat and vegetables, and maybe limit himself to just five, or perhaps six, buns a day.

A few weeks later, Mr Brown went back to his doctor to moan that dieting really didn't suit him. He felt desperately tired and out of breath all the time, and unless he wrapped up warm every day he was miserably cold. The doctor took a blood sample and, on testing, his red blood cell count was shown to be only 3.8 million cells mm^{-3} and his haemoglobin concentration had fallen to 9.5 g dl^{-1} (a normal red blood cell count is about 5.4 million cells mm^{-3} and a normal haemoglobin concentration is about 15.0 g dl^{-1}).

 16. What was Mr Brown probably suffering from?

17. What effect would Mr Brown's condition have on his erythropoietin levels?

18. How could Mr Brown's condition be treated?

■ Destruction of old red blood cells

As the red blood cells age they become increasingly fragile. Eventually they rupture, often as they distort to get through narrow sinusoids, particularly in the liver and the spleen. The debris from ruptured cells is phagocytosed by the fixed macrophages (*Kupffer cells*) lining the sinusoids of the liver, and the haemoglobin is split into the protein component and haem. The protein part is deaminated by the hepatocytes, while the haem group is split to give iron, which is retained, and a residue which forms the bile pigment *bilirubin*. Most bilirubin is passed out in the bile to be excreted via the faeces, although some can pass into the blood and be excreted via the urine. The iron may be stored in the liver as *ferritin* until required to make more haemoglobin, or it may be attached to a plasma protein called *transferrin* to be transported by the blood to the red bone marrow and spleen, where it may also be stored as ferritin.

19. Jaundice is a yellowing of the skin due to excess bilirubin in the blood, as a result of excessive breakdown of red blood cells and haemoglobin. Why is jaundice so common in new born babies?

■ LEUCOCYTES

Leucocytes (white blood cells) may be subdivided according to their appearance into: *granulocytes*, which have granular cytoplasm and multi-lobed nuclei (i.e. they are polymorphonuclear); and *agranulocytes*, which have non-granular cytoplasm and either an oval or a horseshoe-shaped nucleus.

The granulocytes are further subdivided into four types; *basophils, eosinophils, neutrophils* and *macrophages* depending on whether their cytoplasmic granules are basophilic (stain blue with basic stains like basic fuchsin), eosinophilic (stain red with the acidic stain eosin), or neutrophilic (do not stain strongly with either basic or acidic stains). The agranulocytes are divided into monocytes and lymphocytes. Table 1.3 summarises the five types of leucocyte, their size, function and relative proportions in the blood.

Granulocytes and monocytes are produced by the red bone marrow, while lymphocytes originate in lymphoid tissue, such as the spleen, lymph

Cell type	Relative proportions (%)	Size (m)	Function
Granulocytes Basophils Eosinophils Neutrophils	0.5 - 1% 2 - 4 % 70%	8 - 10 10 - 12 10 - 12	Counter-allergens Counter-allergens Phagocytosis
Agranulocytes Monocytes Lymphocytes	3 - 8% 20 - 25%	14 - 19 7 - 15	Phagocytosis Immunity

Table 1.3 Characteristics of different white blood cells

nodes, and tonsils. All the white cells can leave the circulation by diapedesis. White cells can there- fore be found in all tissues and fluids of the body, sometimes in large numbers.

• *Neutrophils* (Fig.1.11(b)) are actively amoeboid cells (and like an amoeba, they move about using pseudopodia). They are the major phagocytes against bacteria during infections. In their cytoplasmic granules are packets of digestive en- zymes (lysozymes) for breaking down the ingested bacteria. Neutrophils are attracted to inflamed tissue by *chemotaxis* (i.e. movement in response to a chemical stimulus), and show active diapedesis.

• *Eosinophils* (Fig.1.11(c)) produce antihistamines which combat the effects of allergens, and which break down antigen-antibody complexes. Large numbers are released if parasitic worms or flukes invade the body. Eosinophils are also phagocytic.

• *Basophils* (Fig.1.11(d)) leave the circulation quickly to enter the tissues where they are known as mast cells. The mast cells release antihistamines to counteract the effects of irritants that cause allergies. In the blood, basophils release *heparin* to suppress unnecessary clotting and *serotonin* which makes capillaries more 'leaky' during infection, so that phagocytes can escape more readily.

• *Monocytes* (Fig.1.11(e)) have horseshoe-shaped nuclei and a few eosinophilic granules in their cytoplasm. They are very strong phagocytes against bacteria and only remain in the circulation for a few hours before undergoing diapedesis.

• *Lymphocytes* (Fig.1.11(f)) have large oval nuclei with very little cytoplasm. They are involved in the production of antibodies, which are special

proteins (gamma globulins) that neutralise *antigens*. An antigen is defined as any substance that will initiate and stimulate the formation of antibodies, examples being the 'foreign' proteins of tissue and organ transplants, or the protein coats of viruses and bacteria. The actions of lymphocytes and antibodies is known as the im- mune response.

■ THE IMMUNE RESPONSE

Lymphocytes are formed from cells in the fetal red bone marrow called *lymphocyte stem cells*. Before birth the lymphocytes migrate either to lymphoid tissue where they remain as B-lymphocytes, or to the thymus gland in the upper chest and lower neck where they are modified to become T-lymphocytes. As the thymus gets smaller and eventually virtually disappears during *puberty*, T-lymphocytes migrate again to join up with the B-lymphocytes in the other lymphoid tissue. T-lymphocytes are concerned with directly attacking and destroying foreign cells (*cellular immunity*). B-lymphocytes are concerned with *humoral or chemical immunity* producing antibodies to attack the foreign cells.

■ Cellular immunity
If an antigen enters the body it is phagocytosed by macrophages. These 'present' the antigens to the T-lymphocytes, some of which recognise the antigen as foreign and become sensitised. Sensi- tised T-cells increase in size and divide by mitosis, producing a clone of cells, which then differentiate into four types with different functions.

• *Killer T-cells* migrate to the site of infection, attach to the invading cells, virus or bacteria, and secrete toxic substances (probably lysozyme) which destroy the foreign body.
• *Helper T-cells* act with the B-lymphocytes, helping them to produce antibodies.
• *Suppressor T-cells* regulate the actions of killer T-cells and B-cells, limiting their activities to foreign antigens only.
• *Memory T-cells* are programmed to memorise the original antigen so that a rapid response can be made if a second infection by the same antigen happens, even if this is years later. This is known as *active immunity*.

■ Humoral immunity

Antigens are also 'presented' to B-lymphocytes by macrophages after phagocytosis. Certain B-cells divide rapidly by mitosis to produce a clone of cells which differentiate into two types:
• *Plasma cells* leave the lymphoid tissue to enter the bloodstream. These cells secrete antibodies specific to the antigens, at a phenomenal rate (about 20 000 antibody molecules every ten seconds). The antibodies attach to the antigens, inactivating, clumping or destroying them.
• *Memory cells* remain in the lymphoid tissue. If the same antigen is encountered again, they produce an extremely rapid humoral immune response.

 20. What immunisations are commonly given to children to protect them?

21. Has your (or your neighbour's) dog or cat been immunised, and if so, against what?

22. The AIDS virus (HIV) attacks the helper T-cells and destroys them. What effect will this have on the immune response?

■ BLOOD GROUPS

The cell membranes of erythrocytes have antigenic proteins called *agglutinogens*. The particular proteins present are genetically controlled and give rise to blood group systems, the two most important of which are the ABO system and the rhesus system.

■ The ABO blood group system

The ABO system concerns the presence or absence of two agglutinogens, proteins A and B on the surface of red blood cells. In group A people, all red blood cells carry agglutinogen A, while in group B people, the red blood cells carry agglutinogen B. In group AB people, the red blood cells carry both A and B agglutinogens, and in group O people, neither agglutinogen is present.

Blood plasma contains particular antibodies called *agglutinins* which are also genetically determined. Agglutinin A (anti-A) will cause the clumping together (agglutination) of red blood cells containing agglutinogen A, and agglutinin B (anti-B) will clump together red blood cells containing agglutinogen B. You do not possess agglutinins against your own erythrocytes, but you do have agglutinins to attack any foreign agglutinogens, in other words, group A people possess anti-B and vice versa. Table 1.4 summarises this information.

When giving a person a blood transfusion, care must be taken to match the blood correctly so that the recipient's agglutinins (in their plasma) will not clump the red blood cells of the donated blood. If this occurs, then clumped red blood cells may block small blood vessels, such as in the glomeruli of the kidney, and result in the death of the recipient.

Blood Group	Antigen on red cells	Antibody in plasma	Can receive whole blood from
A	A	Anti-B	Groups A and O
B	B	Anti-A	Groups B and O
AB	A and B	Neither	Groups A, B, AB and O
O	Neither	Anti-A and anti-B	Group O

Table 1.4 The ABO blood group system

The table indicates that group AB people (who do not possess anti-A or anti-B antibodies) can, in theory, receive blood from all other groups, so they are called *universal recipients*. Similarly, group O blood can theoretically be given to any recipient, so a group O person is a *universal donor*.

 23. A road accident victim with group AB blood is given an emergency blood transfusion with group O blood. Why don't the anti-A and anti-B antibodies in the plasma of the donated blood agglutinate the accident victim's red blood cells?

Different races of people in different parts of the world exhibit different frequencies of the same blood groups. This is illustrated in Table 1.5.

Blood Group	Descent (%)	
	United Kingdom, Western Europe	USA. Africa
A	42	29
B	9	17
AB	3	4
O	46	50

Table 1.5 The percentage of ABO blood groups present in different populations

■ The Rhesus blood group system
The rhesus sytem depends on the presence or absence of an antigenic protein, first discovered in rhesus monkeys. Individuals whose red blood cells possess the rhesus agglutinogen are called rhesus positive (Rh$^+$) and make up about 85% of the UK indigenous population. Fifteen per cent of individuals have no rhesus antigens and are termed rhesus negative (Rh$^-$). Under normal circumstances their plasma does not contain anti-rhesus agglutinins (anti-D), which only develop if the immune response is invoked by the introduction of Rh$^+$ red blood cells into their circulation. This might happen in two possible situations:

• *Transfusions.* A Rh$^-$ person may receive a transfusion of Rh$^+$ blood in error. The immune response is activated, and anti-D antibodies are synthesised. This initial immune response is slow, and the transfused red blood cells will have died before serious agglutination can occur (their average life is only 120 days remember). If however,

the same mistake happens again, the memory cells are able to stimulate a rapid production of large quantities of anti-D. The transfused red blood cells will be agglutinated and the patient will either die or suffer an extremely severe reaction.

• *Pregnancy.* Where a mother is Rh$^-$ and the father is Rh$^+$ there is a 50% chance that the baby will be Rh$^+$. Towards the end of pregnancy the placenta starts to age, and some fetal Rh$^+$ red blood cells may leak into the mother's blood, stimulating her immune system to synthesise anti-D. The process is slow, and if this is her first pregnancy with a Rh$^+$ baby, the child will be born before sufficient anti-D can be made to cause a problem.
A second pregnancy with a Rh$^+$ baby, however, is more serious. As soon as fetal cells leak across the placenta, the mother rapidly produces large amounts of anti-D which can return across the placenta into the baby. These agglutinate and haemolyse (burst) the fetal red blood cells, leading either to fetal death, or to haemolytic disease of the newborn child. If the latter, the newborn infant can only be saved by a complete change of blood by transfusion immediately after birth.
The above situation is easily avoided. If the Rh$^-$ mother is given an injection of anti-D immediately after the first Rh$^+$ child is born, the injected antibodies will 'mop up' any fetal red blood cells in her circulation and so prevent her immune response being activated at all.

 24. Is there likely to be a problem if a Rh$^+$ mother bears a Rh$^-$ baby? Why?

■ HAEMOSTASIS

Haemostasis means stopping bleeding. If a blood vessel is damaged in any way, then a sequence of mechanisms is initiated with the aim of preventing or minimising blood loss.

■ Vascular spasm
All blood vessels except capillaries contain a layer of smooth muscle in their walls. This muscle layer reacts to vessel damage by immediately contracting, and by remaining contracted for up to 30 minutes. The volume of blood flowing through the damaged portion is thus reduced while the other haemostatic mechanisms operate.

Platelet plug formation

If the endothelial lining of a blood vessel is ruptured, the underlying collagen of the fibrous layer is exposed to the bloodstream. Similarly if your skin is cut or grazed, blood from dermal capillaries is released on to collagen in the skin. Platelets that come into contact with collagen become enlarged and sticky, and then actually stick to the collagen fibres with the expenditure of energy from ATP. These platelets release substances that cause other platelets to adhere to them, and soon the rupture in the vessel wall becomes covered by a plug of platelets. This is sufficient to stop bleeding if it is a small vessel. Although the plug is initially loose, it becomes strengthened by fibrin threads after clotting.

Coagulation

Coagulation is a complex process, involving platelets and at least 17 factors from the plasma. It can be simplified to a sequence of three main stages:
• The enzyme, *thromboplastin,* must be formed first. It can be released into the blood by damaged tissues, or formed by the disintegration of platelets within the blood.
• Thromboplastin catalyses the conversion of a plasma protein called *prothrombin* into another enzyme, *thrombin*. This conversion requires the presence of *calcium ions*.
• Thombin, again in the presence of calcium ions, catalyses the conversion of the soluble plasma protein *fibrinogen* into insoluble threads of *fibrin*. These threads plus entangled blood cells enmesh within the platelet plug. The plug is thus reinforced and the whole structure is called a *clot*. This should stop the bleeding.

One of the coagulation factors produced by normal platelets is *factor 8*. This is anti-haemophilic globulin (AHG). People who are unable to make this because of a sex-linked gene defect are haemophiliacs, and lack the ability to clot blood. (See *Biology Advanced Studies - Genetics and Evolution*.)

Clot retraction

In the hours and days after clotting, the fibrin threads gradually contract and cross-bond with one another to pull the walls of the damaged vessel closer, and to retract (shrink) the clot. More fibrin is added as some platelets within the clot disintegrate, and the whole clot thickens and hardens to form a *scab*. As the clot retracts, a fluid called serum is forced out of it. This is the plasma that was in the clot minus the protein clotting factors such as prothrombin and fibrinogen. The scab acts as a 'scaffold' under which the vessel wall or other tissue can be repaired.

Fibrinolysis

Fibrinolysis is the dissolving of the clot/scab once tissue repair is complete. Scabs on the body surface can of course fall off, but those deep in the tissue have to be broken down by enzymes called *plasmins*. These are formed from precursor plasma proteins called *plasminogens* which are activated by chemicals released from damaged tissues.

 25. Suggest three functions of haemostasis.

This chapter began with a case study where a tumour was produced because in one tissue the rate of cell growth and division had increased to abnormal levels - a case of cancer of the cervix of the womb. There are many other cancer types and other tissues and organs can be affected, including stomach, skin, liver, spleen, testis, prostate, lung and breast. Intensive and expensive research has found ways of treating some of them. Cytologists have found some genes (and named them *oncogenes*) that can be switched on to transform normal cells into malignant cells. These cells' rate of cell division is changed and they lose the ability to differentiate and to stick together. Although oncogenes cause some cancers, other risk factors can add to the chances of cancers developing. For instance, lung cancers are much more common in cigarette smokers. Radiation and certain chemicals also have a *carcinogenic* effect. It is known that some types of cancer are more common in older people - possibly as a result of the accumulation of risk factors and damage to their DNA.

An interesting development in the research for cancer treatment has come about as biotechnologists are able to genetically engineer DNA and to grow cells in tissue culture. Some of the cultured cells have a code inserted for the manufacture of an antibody (known as a monoclonal antibody). Several promising techniques are being tested. They depend on the fact that the monoclonal antibody can be injected into the bloodstream where it will travel around the body until it recognises and sticks to a cancer cell. If the antibody has molecules of a cancer cell-killing (*cytotoxic*) drug attached to it then only the tumour cells will be killed. This type of research must give hope that future cancer treatments will have a greater chance of success.

2 SUPPORT AND MOVEMENT

■ CASE STUDY: A NATURAL ATHLETE

Rob Smith was a first class sprinter noted for his fine muscular physique and athletic prowess. During routine drug testing at the national championships however, his blood was found to contain traces of Anapolon 50, an **anabolic steroid**, and he was disqualified. The drug is normally used by doctors to treat various forms of anaemia because it stimulates red blood cell formation. It would therefore improve the ventilatory efficiency of an athlete, and as it also promotes protein synthesis, it could enable the athlete to develop more muscle, making him (or her) a stronger competitor. Anabolic steroids also have serious side effects, and their prolonged use may result in kidney disease, leukaemia, cancers of the liver and prostate gland in men, and masculinisation in women. Three years after Mr Smith's disqualification, he developed liver cancer and died.

Q 1. What particular qualities might a successful athlete have, in terms of body structure and physiology?

2. Suggest ways in which Mr Smith could have improved his performance without resorting to illegal and dangerous drugs.

■ VOLUNTARY MOVEMENT

Voluntary movements include large locomotory movements such as running or walking, and also small rapid adjustments in position such as the movements involved in playing a musical instrument.

anabolic a synthetic or building up process of metabolism, such as protein synthesis; steroid meaning a lipid or fatty type of substance

voluntary nervous system the conscious control of body actions by the brain (unlike involuntary reflex actions and the involuntary regulation of processes such as heartbeat)

These movements are under the control of the **voluntary nervous system**. Voluntary movements occur by the contraction of striated (skeletal or voluntary) muscles against the bones of the skeleton about a joint. Striated muscle can undergo rapid contraction at will, the contraction being either isotonic in which muscle length shortens but the tone (tension) stays the same, or isometric in which muscle tone increases but the muscle length stays the same.

Q 3. Why is locomotion important to the survival of animals?

■ STRUCTURE OF STRIATED MUSCLE

The smallest working units in striated muscle are called *sarcomeres*, which can be seen in Fig.2.1(a). Each sarcomere contains dark and light bands, which are due to the arrangement of the contractile proteins, *actin* and *myosin*, which make up the sarcomere structure. (This is described below under 'protein filaments'.)

A large number of sarcomeres are arranged end to end to make a *fibril*. Fibrils are lined up side by side to form a fibre in such a way that the dark and light bands of the sarcomeres correspond resulting in cross-stripes (striations) when viewed under the light microscope. Hence the name striated muscle. The structure of a fibre can be seen in Fig.2.1(b).

■ Muscle fibres

A muscle fibre is not divided into cells, but instead forms a *syncytium*, which means a unit of cytoplasm (known in this case as *sarcoplasm*) with many nuclei. There are many mitochondria within the fibrils to generate sufficient adenosine triphosphate (ATP), the compound which fuels muscle contraction. The outer membrane of the fibre is called the *sarcolemma*, and is connected to an extensive system of membrane-bound channels. These make up the *sarcoplasmic reticulum* which is an important reservoir of

(a) *Sarcomere* (*light microscope*)

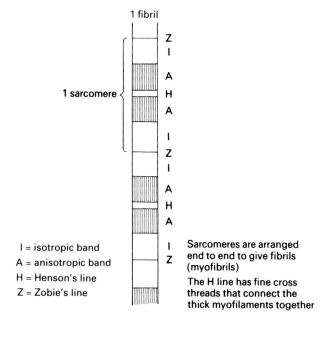

1 fibril

1 sarcomere

Z
I
A
H
A
I
Z
I
A
H
A
I
Z

I = isotropic band
A = anisotropic band
H = Henson's line
Z = Zobie's line

Sarcomeres are arranged
end to end to give fibrils
(myofibrils)

The H line has fine cross
threads that connect the
thick myofilaments together

(b) *One fibre* (*longitudinal section*)

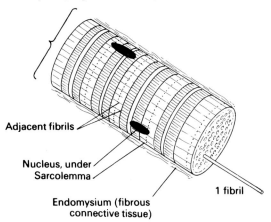

Adjacent fibrils

Nucleus, under
Sarcolemma

Endomysium (fibrous
connective tissue)

1 fibril

Fibres are arranged side by side into bundles or fasiculi
These fasiculi are arranged side by side to make the
belly of the muscle The collagen within the endomycium,
perimycium and epimycium is continuous with that in
the tendons attaching the muscle to the bone, and from
there, with the collagen of the periosteum and
Sharpey fibres of the bone

Figure 2.1 Histology of striated muscle.

(c) *Muscle belly* (*transverse section*)

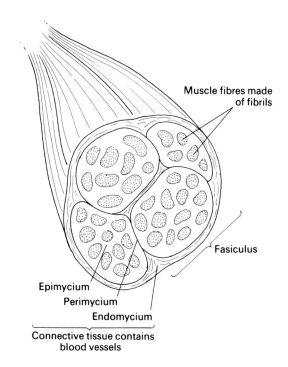

Muscle fibres made
of fibrils

Fasiculus

Epimycium
Perimycium
Endomycium

Connective tissue contains
blood vessels

(d) *Skeletal muscle* (*general anatomy*)

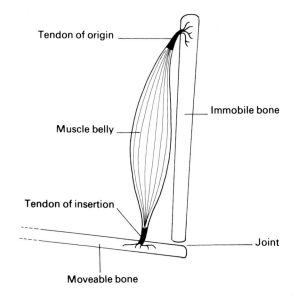

Tendon of origin

Immobile bone

Muscle belly

Tendon of insertion

Joint

Moveable bone

(e) *Sarcomere (electron microscope)*

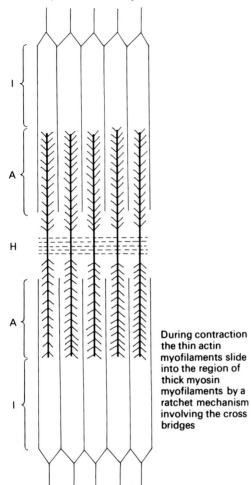

During contraction the thin actin myofilaments slide into the region of thick myosin myofilaments by a ratchet mechanism involving the cross bridges

(f) *Protein filaments of skeletal muscle*

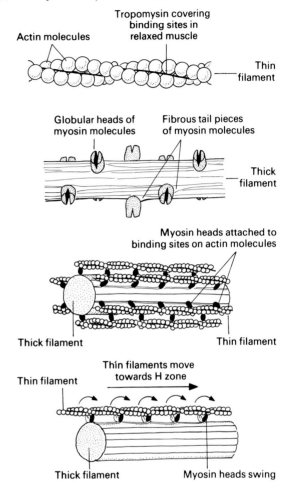

Figure 2.1 (continued) Histology of striated muscle.

calcium ions that are needed for the contraction mechanism. The reticulum can run the length of a fibre or can run across fibres forming *T-tubules*.

Each fibre is encased in a sheath of white fibrous connective tissue called an *endomycium*, and each group of fibres is bound into a bundle (*fasciculus*) by another similar sheath called a *perimycium*. Finally all the fasciculi are held together to form the muscle belly, by an outer sheath of connective tissue called the *epimycium* (Fig.2.1(c)). The white fibres of all three levels of sheath continue beyond the ends of the muscle belly to form the tendons that anchor the muscle to bone (Fig.2.1(d)). These fibres contain large amounts of the protein *collagen* (see page 28) which gives tensile strength to the tissues, preventing them from tearing under the stresses and strains of muscular activity. The sheaths also carry the extensive blood and nerve supply, and lymph drainage ducts of the muscle.

■ **Protein filaments**
The electron microscope reveals the filaments of contractile protein that make up each sarcomere and these can be seen in Figs. 2.1(e) and (f). The *Z lines* (Zobie's lines) at the end consist of *alpha-actinin*, and from either side of these, thin filaments of *actin* stretch into the sarcomere with thicker filaments of *myosin* between them. Where myosin is present the sarcomere appears dark (the *A bands*), and where only actin is present it appears light (the *I bands*).

The *thin filaments* are composed of many globular actin molecules forming two long threads that spiral round each other. At each twist there is a point (myosin binding site) where myosin can become attached. In a relaxed muscle these binding sites are covered by *tropomyosin*, a fibrous protein that is wrapped round the actin filament.

Each *thick filament* is composed of about 200 myosin molecules. The structure of a myosin molecule is unusual in that it is part fibrous and part globular, consisting of a fibrous tailpiece, with two globular 'heads' at one end. The heads project from the sides of the filament and contain groups that enable them to attach to the myosin binding sites on the actin filaments. This allows contraction to occur. The heads also contain the *ATPase* enzyme for releasing energy from ATP, in the presence of calcium ions which are required for the enzyme to function.

■ FUNCTIONING OF STRIATED MUSCLE

■ All-or-none principle
Muscle contraction results from nerve impulses transmitted along *motor neurones* to the muscle. A single motor neurone and all the muscle fibres it stimulates comprise a *motor* unit. If stimulated, all muscle fibres of a motor unit (Fig.2.2(a)) contract to their fullest extent. Partial contraction is impossible. This does not mean that the whole muscle contracts, as it consists of many motor units of various sizes. The weakest stimulus from a neurone that can initiate contraction is called the *threshold stimulus* (see also page 82).

■ Depolarisation
As impulses arrive at each neuromuscular junction, the transmitter substance *acetylcholine* is released in **vesicles** from the membrane of the motor neurone. It attaches to receptors on the sarcolemma allowing *depolarisation* to occur. A wave of depolarisation then passes along the fibre causing the sarcoplasmic reticulum to release *calcium ions* into the sarcoplasm. The wave of depolarisation does not extend to nearby fibres because of the insulating effect of the endomycium. This means that for the whole muscle to contract, all motor units must receive impulses.

---

vesicles small fluid-filled sacs formed by pinching off from the Golgi body - a means of secreting substances from cells

---

(a) *Motor unit*

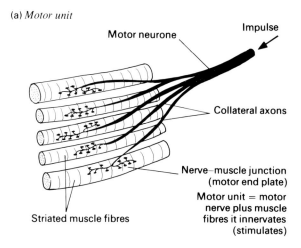

(b) *Motor end plate* (*light microscope*)

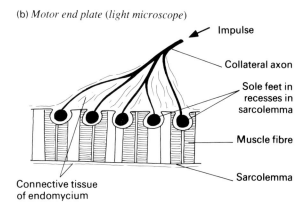

(c) *Diagram of sole foot* (*electron microscope*)

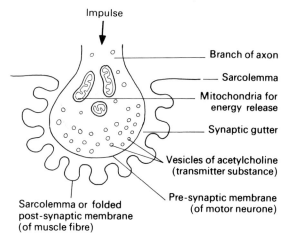

Figure 2.2

Q 4. Owing to the insulating endomycium, the simplest response of striated muscle is a twitch of a single muscle fibre. What advantage might that be to the animal?

5. How is the wave of contraction spread through cardiac muscle? (See page 38.)

6. Why does acetycholine only act on the sarcolemma for a few ten thousandths of a second? (See page 81.)

■ **Ratchet mechanism**

The accumulation of calcium ions in the sarcoplasm displaces tropomyosin, and thus exposes the myosin binding sites on the actin filaments. Using energy from ATP, myosin heads attach to the binding sites to form 'cross-bridges' between the filaments. More energy from ATP is then used to alter the angle at which the myosin heads project from the filament. This draws the actin filaments further into the dark myosin band, so shortening the sarcomere. This is the *ratchet mechanism* which is responsible for isotonic contraction (Fig.2.1(f)). This can be repeated many times giving up to a 30% contraction in the length of the sarcomere.

As the muscle fibre repolarises, calcium ions are pumped back into the sarcoplasmic reticulum and T-tubules using ATP. The myosin heads uncouple, and tropomyosin returns to its former position covering the binding sites. The actin filaments thus draw back out of the myosin zone and the sarcomere lengthens.

The high proportion of mitochondria in muscle tissue means that when a muscle is resting, it produces surplus ATP. Some of this is stored attached to the myosin filaments, while the remainder reacts with creatine to give energy-rich creatine phosphate. Enough creatine phosphate is stored in the muscle to enable a strong contraction when stimulated during the several second's delay which it takes to speed up glycolysis and the other cellular respiration processes. This can later be converted back to ATP, releasing a high 'surge' of energy, when the muscle has to undergo sudden strenuous contractions, such as when Rob Smith (see page 21) leaves the starting blocks.

ATP + creatine ⟶ creatine phosphate
+ ADP (adenosine diphosphate)

■ **Fast and slow muscle fibres**

Striated muscle tissue is not uniform in all parts of the body.

• *Fast muscle fibres* occur where the speed of response is more important than producing sustained contraction, for example in the external eye muscles. There is less myoglobin, and fewer mitochondria and capillaries in this muscle, which is also termed *white muscle*, but the sarcoplasmic reticulum is particularly extensive to allow faster release of calcium ions. The muscle can therefore contract faster, though it only remains contracted for about 0.001 second.

• *Slow muscle fibres* occur in the limb muscle, where contraction must be sustained long enough to move a bone. Such muscle is termed *red muscle* because it contains much more red myoglobin, numerous mitochondria and an extensive capillary network. The fibres remain contracted for about 0.03 second after receiving an impulse. This was the sort of muscle that Rob Smith was hoping to develop by using Anapolon 50 (see page 21).

Q 7. If some acetylcholine receptors on the sarcolemma of a neuromuscular junction are damaged, then depolarisation and hence contraction become difficult. Do you think that white muscle or red muscle would be affected first by this? Why?

■ **Isometric contraction**

Striated muscles are also responsible for the maintenance of posture and balance, under the control of the cerebellum. They do so by isometric contraction, which increases muscle *tone* while the length of the muscle stays the same. Thus bones are held in a certain position rather than actually being moved. The degree of tone (tonicity) in a muscle is sensed by special nerve receptors called *muscle spindles*, which are examples of *proprioceptors* (for other receptors - see Chapter 7).

■ **Muscular dystrophy**

Muscular dystrophy involves the progressive wasting and degeneration of striated muscle fibres on both sides of the body. It is not certain exactly what causes the disease, though several factors have been implicated, such as genetic defects, protein deficiency and faulty potassium metabolism. There is at present no cure, and no specific drug therapy available. The development of the condition can be delayed, if the sufferer keeps mobile for as long as possible.

■ STRUCTURE AND FUNCTION OF SMOOTH MUSCLE

Smooth muscle is also known as visceral muscle or involuntary muscle, since it is involved with movement within body organs (*viscera*) and it is under the control of the *autonomic nervous system*. Smooth muscle cells contract and relax slowly, taking up to 60 seconds to reach full contraction, and then holding the contracted state for many minutes before fatiguing. In the walls of blood vessels, the tone of smooth muscle helps to regulate blood flow and blood pressure, and in the alimentary canal, urinary tubes and reproductive tract, smooth muscle propels materials along. Propulsion occurs by *peristalsis*, which is a slow, rhythmic contraction followed by relaxation, with the separate circular and longitudinal coats of smooth muscle acting *antagonistically* (i.e. as one contracts, the other relaxes).

Smooth muscle cells (Fig.2.3) can easily be separated, or teased out, from one another. They are seen under the light microscope as long spindle-shaped cells with tapering ends, and are between 50 and 100 micrometres long and 2 to 5 micrometres in diameter. In the widest part of the cell, there is a central sausage-shaped nucleus, at either end of which is a 'cap' of cytoplasm containing numerous mitochondria. Under the light microscope, the cytoplasm appears uniform

apart from a faint impression of filaments running lengthwise. These filaments are revealed clearly with the electron microscope, and shown to be attached to discs on the inside of the cell membrane. The discs are made of alpha-actinin, and the filaments are almost certainly actin and myosin. The contraction mechanism is similar to that of the sarcomere of striated muscle, and as the cell shortens it gets fatter.

Q 8. What factors must be present in smooth muscle for the reaction of myosin with actin to take place?

Adjacent cells interlock by their tapering ends to form sheets and bundles of muscle, with the alpha-actinin discs of one cell firmly bound to those of the adjacent cells. The cells are surrounded by loose connective tissue, and are served by a network (*plexus*) of automatic nerves rather than each cell having its own individual neurone. Though the tissue can contract and relax of its own accord, the rate and force of contraction is modified by the *sympathetic* and *parasympathetic* nervous systems.

Sympathetic stimulation will, for example, increase the contraction of the pupil dilator muscle in the iris, widening the pupil and allowing more light to enter the eye, while parasympathetic stimulation increases contraction of the pupil constrictor muscle and has the reverse effect.

The tone of smooth muscle may also be affected by hormones. During pregnancy, the high concentration of *progesterone* inhibits the contraction of the smooth muscle of the uterus, so preventing spontaneous abortion. This inhibition is removed as the pregnancy reaches full term and the ageing placenta secretes less progesterone. Raised levels of the hormone *oxytocin* then stimulate contractions of the uterine muscle while relaxing the cervical smooth muscle (opening the birth canal) so the baby can be born.

■ CONVERTING THE FORCE OF CONTRACTION INTO MOVEMENT

When considering how the contraction of striated muscles can be converted into movement, there are three main points to bear in mind.
• Firstly, isotonic contraction causes the muscle fibres to *shorten*, and it is this shortening that must be harnessed in order to move one bone relative to another.
• Secondly, to achieve this, one of the bones has to

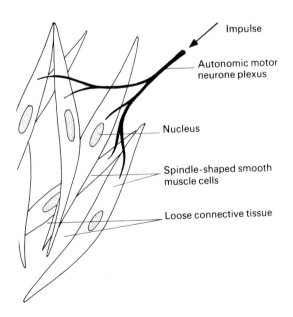

Impulse

Autonomic motor neurone plexus

Nucleus

Spindle-shaped smooth muscle cells

Loose connective tissue

Figure 2.3 Smooth muscle cells

be kept *fixed* by the isometric contraction of other muscles.

• Thirdly, any movement across a joint involves the actions of a group of muscles, each with a specific role to play.

These points can be illustrated with reference to the muscles that move the elbow joint, (Fig.2.4). The elbow is a hinge joint which has restricted movement. It can either *flex*, in which the angle between the upper arm and the forearm gets narrower, or *extend*, in which the angle widens. These two movements are initiated by the isotonic contraction of a pair of *antagonistic muscles* known as the *prime movers* of the joint. The prime mover that contracts to flex the arm is the biceps muscle, which has its tendon of insertion on the radius, while the prime mover that extends the arm is the triceps, with its tendon of insertion on the olecranon process of the ulna. As the biceps contracts, the triceps must relax, and vice versa. The biceps and triceps are antagonistic in this action.

The movements are not this simple, however, since the tendons of *origin* of both muscles cross the highly mobile shoulder joint between the head of the humerus and the *glenoid cavity* of the scapula. The biceps has two tendons of origin, both on the scapula, and the triceps has three, two on the scapula and one on the shaft of the humerus. Thus when either muscle contracts, it is possible that the shoulder joint could move rather than the elbow. To prevent this, the shoulder joint is fixed in place during elbow movements by the isometric contraction of several other muscles. Such muscles are termed *fixators*. Two of these for the shoulder are the supraspinatus and infraspinatus muscles, which have their tendons of insertion on the humerus and tendons of origin on the scapula. Under different circumstances, fixator muscles can become prime movers. During movement of the shoulder joint, for example, the supraspinatus and infraspinatus may contract isotonically to rotate the joint, other muscles then acting as fixators, and during movements of the wrist and fingers, the biceps and triceps act as fixators of the elbow.

Q 9. Which bone or joint do you think should be fixed in place when the shoulder joint is moved?

10. The lifting of the fore-arm by the biceps is a third order lever system, i.e.

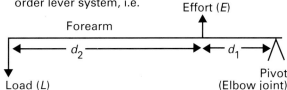

According to the laws of physics relating to levers: $E \times d_1 = L \times d_2$. If $d_1 = 4$ cm and $d_2 = 28$ cm, what effort must be applied by the biceps to lift a shopping bag (the load) weighing 12 kg?

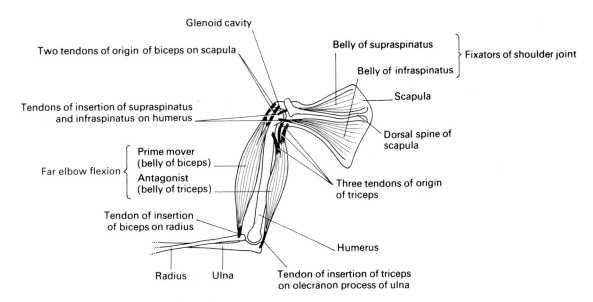

Figure 2.4 Bones and muscles involved in movement at the elbow joint

If you answered Question 10, you will see that even when lifting a moderate weight of only 12 kg, huge stresses are placed on the muscle, its tendons and the bones. The tissues must therefore be designed to be able to withstand stretching, shearing or compressing strains depending on the particular actions involved.

■ STRUCTURAL TISSUES

■ The role of collagen
Collagen is one of the most important structural proteins in the body. It is a fibrous protein, synthesised by cells called *fibroblasts*, and its individual fibres are inelastic, with a very high tensile strength. This means that they can resist pulling strains without breaking.

Areolar tissue is the basic packing tissue found in organs. It holds structures together, allows dimension changes, and carries the blood and lymph vessels and nerves within the organs. In areolar tissue collagen fibres run a wavy course in all directions, allowing the tissue to be stretched in all directions without tearing. A second fibrous protein, *elastin*, is present which is elastic and so can recoil to return the tissue to its original size and shape once the stretching force is removed. The fibres in muscle sheaths are arranged like this, enabling shape changes during muscle contraction and relaxation.

■ Tendons
At each end of a muscle, all the collagen fibres of the muscle sheaths group together to form one or more *tendons*. The fibres are now arranged in parallel bundles with no elastin present, making each tendon an extremely strong structure. Tendons attach muscle to bone, and at the bone surface the tendon collagen fibres are continuous with those of the *periosteum* (bone sheath), which are in turn continuous with the Sharpey fibres of the bone substance itself (see page 30). This union between tendon and bone is very hard to break.

Q 11. The Achilles tendon behind the ankle has a cross-sectional area of about 120 mm². Given that most tendons can withstand pulling forces up to about 9 kg per mm², what would be the maximum load the Achilles tendon could withstand?

Although tendons are excellent at withstanding tugging forces, they will crumple and fold if they are compressed, or squashed by a heavy weight. To withstand compression, collagen fibres must therefore be enclosed in a *matrix* of surrounding material, forming either cartilage or bone. The bundles of collagen are not normally visible in this matrix, but there are laboratory techniques available that will demonstrate their presence.

■ Cartilage structure
Cartilage (Fig.2.5) contains active and inactive cells. The active cells are called *chondroblasts* (from the Greek word *chondros mean*ing gristle) and these secrete the matrix. They later becoming inactive *chondrocytes* surrounded by mature matrix.

(a)

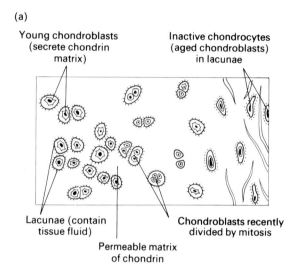

Young chondroblasts (secrete chondrin matrix)

Inactive chondrocytes (aged chondroblasts) in lacunae

Lacunae (contain tissue fluid)

Chondroblasts recently divided by mitosis

Permeable matrix of chondrin

(b)

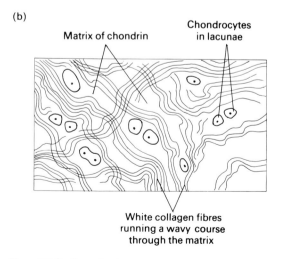

Matrix of chondrin

Chondrocytes in lacunae

White collagen fibres running a wavy course through the matrix

Figure 2.5 Cartilage structure

Chondroblasts can be seen at the edges of a piece of growing cartilage, but as more matrix is formed, the cells are pushed further away from each other. They lie in small spaces in the matrix called *lacunae*, and as they are capable of dividing by mitosis, there are frequently two or four cells per lacuna. As cartilage grows, the connective tissue around it is compressed to form a cartilage sheath.

In addition to collagen, chondroblasts also secrete substances called glycosaminoglycans (*GAGs*). These have long backbones made up of a polymer of hyaluronic acid (a glucose derivative), with many protein side-arms to which molecules of chondroitin sulphate and keratin sulphate are attached. The latter carry negative charges that repel one another, so the molecule is held open like a bottle brush, containing bound water in the spaces. The resulting structure is very springy and resilient, able to resist deforming forces such as compression.

The complete matrix is called *chondrin*, and the collagen fibres within it have definite orientations to withstand the forces operating on the cartilage. Most cartilage lacks blood vessels, but the matrix is permeable to oxygen and nutrients, and also to tissue fluid, which percolates into the lacunae from surrounding capillaries.

■ Types of cartilage
• The commonest type of cartilage is *hyaline cartilage*, which is about 40% collagen as dry mass. The fetal skeleton is first formed of hyaline cartilage, though most of this is replaced by bone fairly quickly. In adults, it remains as the costal cartilages, making strong but flexible links between the rib bones and the sternum, the C-shaped bars which keep the trachea and bronchi open, and the articular cartilages which cover the ends of bones in synovial joints (e.g. the knee) to reduce friction and wear.
• In *fibrocartilage*, the proportion of collagen may be up to 80% of the dry mass. Although the collagen fibres still follow a wavy course through the matrix, they do so in bundles rather than singly. This gives great resilience and strength to the cartilage, which is found in the weight-bearing intervertebral discs, and in and around large tendons where they enter bone.
• *Elastic cartilage* contains many elastic fibres embedded in the matrix with collagen. This makes 'springy' cartilage, as found in the pinna of the outer ear, the epiglottis and the end of the nose.

Q 12. During the ageing process, cartilage often becomes calcified. What effects might this have on the body?

■ The structure of bony tissue
Bone is also built around *collagen*, but about 70% of the matrix is composed of inorganic salts. The basic unit of the matrix is a *spicule*, which consists of a bundle of collagen fibres, known as *Sharpey fibres*, on which are deposited crystals of calcium hydroxyapatite, a mineral of calcium phosphate. This makes the bone rigid and hard, enabling it to resist shearing, compression and tension. In spite of being heavily calcified, it is still a living tissue and may respond to forces acting on it by growing to accommodate them. The breaking stress of long bones is of a similar order to an equivalent volume of cast iron, but iron is three times heavier!

There are three grades of cell in bony tissue, *osteoblasts*, *osteocytes* and *osteoclasts* (from the Greek word *osteos meaning* bone).
• *Osteoblasts* are active cells, secreting collagen, GAGs and the enzymes required for the deposition of calcium phosphate. They are responsible for the formation of the organic part of the matrix and for its mineralisation, and they occur wherever bone is being deposited, usually at the surface of a piece of bone.
• Once an osteoblast is completely surrounded by bone, it can no longer be actively synthetic, and it is then termed an *osteocyte*. These lie in spaces (*lacunae*) in the matrix, and have long strands of cytoplasm which make contact with adjacent osteocytes through small channels (*canaliculi*) in the matrix. Since the matrix is impermeable, tissue fluid and metabolites must pass from cell to cell via the canaliculi and lacunae.
• *Osteoclasts* are large multinucleate cells on the outside of bones. They are responsible for the reabsorption of bone tissue in response to local pressures acting on this tissue.

Q 13. Children that suck their thumbs excessively may force their teeth forward, and require a brace to be fitted by the dentist to correct the problem. Explain this in terms of the forces acting on the teeth, and hence the jawbone, and the responses of osteoblasts and osteoclasts.

14. On the same theme, can you now explain why it is so important that children wear 'sensible' shoes that fit properly?

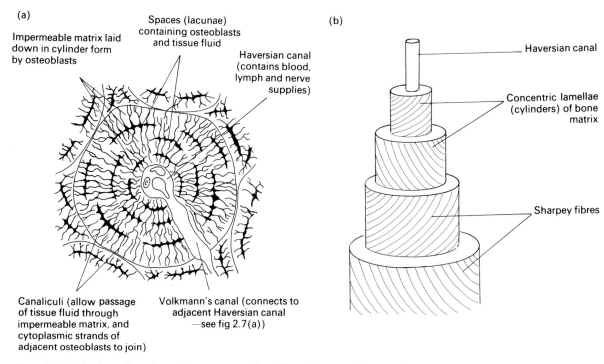

(a)

Impermeable matrix laid down in cylinder form by osteoblasts

Spaces (lacunae) containing osteoblasts and tissue fluid

Haversian canal (contains blood, lymph and nerve supplies)

Canaliculi (allow passage of tissue fluid through impermeable matrix, and cytoplasmic strands of adjacent osteoblasts to join)

Volkmann's canal (connects to adjacent Haversian canal —see fig 2.7(a))

(b)

Haversian canal

Concentric lamellae (cylinders) of bone matrix

Sharpey fibres

Figure 2.6 The histology of bony tissue: (a) transverse section of Haversian system (or osteon), (b) 'exploded' view of the Haversian system showing the Sharpey fibres

■ How bony tissue is built up into bones

The layout of the cells and matrix of bony tissue is not generally random, the commonest and strongest arrangement being into cylindrical units called *osteons*, or *Haversian systems* (Fig.2.6). There is a central Haversian canal that carries the blood vessels, lymphatics and nerves supplying the osteon, and around this canal the matrix is laid down in concentric cylinders. Haversian canals of adjacent osteons are joined directly by *Volkmann's canals*, though tissue fluid is also able to percolate through canaliculi and lacunae from the capillaries. The Sharpey fibres of collagen spiral in different directions in adjacent cylinders. This can be seen in Fig.2.6(b).

Fig.2.7(a) shows how a bone is built up of cylindrical layers (*lamellae*) of the matrix, giving it a 'compound interest' effect of bone strength against compression and tension forces. Fig.2.7(b) illustrates that a bone is in fact an organ. As well as bony tissue, it contains red bone marrow, yellow bone marrow (adipose tissue), cartilage sometimes, and its own blood and nerve supply. Note that the bony tissue around the shaft and heads is *compact*, or solid, while that in the cavity of the bone is said to be *spongy*.

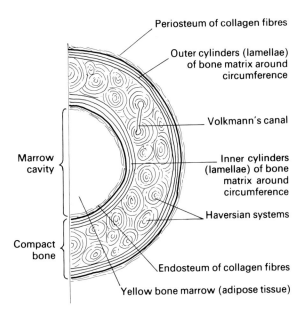

Periosteum of collagen fibres

Outer cylinders (lamellae) of bone matrix around circumference

Volkmann's canal

Inner cylinders (lamellae) of bone matrix around circumference

Haversian systems

Endosteum of collagen fibres

Yellow bone marrow (adipose tissue)

Marrow cavity

Compact bone

Figure 2.7 (a) Transverse section through the shaft of a long bone

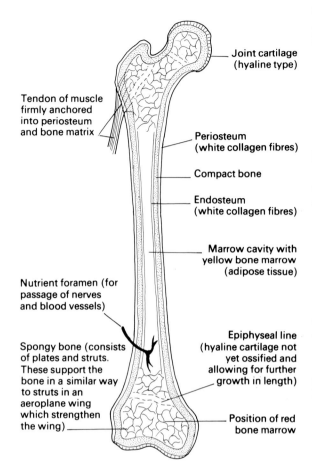

Joint cartilage
(hyaline type)

Tendon of muscle
firmly anchored
into periosteum
and bone matrix

Periosteum
(white collagen fibres)

Compact bone

Endosteum
(white collagen fibres)

Marrow cavity with
yellow bone marrow
(adipose tissue)

Nutrient foramen (for
passage of nerves
and blood vessels)

Epiphyseal line
(hyaline cartilage not
yet ossified and
allowing for further
growth in length)

Spongy bone (consists
of plates and struts.
These support the
bone in a similar way
to struts in an
aeroplane wing
which strengthen
the wing)

Position of red
bone marrow

Figure 2.7 (b) Longitudinal section through a long bone (still capable of longitudinal growth)

■ Vitamins and hormones

The deposition of calcium in bone is regulated by *vitamin D* and by two hormones, *calcitonin* and *parathormone*. Vitamin D promotes bone calcification, and a shortage can result in rickets in children or osteomalacia in adults. Calcitonin is secreted by the thyroid gland and promotes calcification of bone by osteoblast activity, while parathormone is secreted by the parathyroid gland and promotes the release of calcium from bone to the blood by the activity of the osteoclasts.

The activities of osteoblasts and osteoclasts are thus kept balanced by the two hormones as part of homeostasis. There is constant renewal and constant breakdown of bone, ensuring that the collagen protein does not become aged or brittle. A rare genetic defect may upset this balance. It is a condition that can affect the baby in the womb in which undersecretion of parathormone leads to

reduced osteoclast activity. This results in *brittle bone disease*, as the collagen ages and becomes less flexible and less resilient.

 15. What would cause vitamin D deficiency, and how could it be remedied?

16. What are the symptoms of rickets?

■ THE ORGANISATION OF THE SKELETON

Vertebrates have an internal framework of bone, to which muscles are attached at points that give the best mechanical advantage and/or ease of movement. Internal skeletons are known as *endoskeletons*.

17. Refer back to the forearm lever system described in Question 10 on page 27. If the biceps muscle was attached to the radius 12 cm from the elbow joint, instead of 4 cm, (i.e. $d_1 = 12$), would the efficiency of the system by increased or decreased?

■ The human skeleton

The skeleton (Fig.2.8) has three main functions:
• *to support* the body and give it a recognisable shape
• *to allow movement* as the bones and joints form lever systems operated by the attached muscles
• *to protect* vital organs and tissues; e.g. red bone marrow is protected within bones, the brain is protected by the cranium, the spinal cord is protected by the neural arches of the vertebrae, the heart and lungs are protected by the rib cage and sternum, and the uterus (in the female) is protected by the pelvis.

The individual bones of the skeleton may be classified as 'long', 'short', 'flat' or 'irregular' according to their shape. You may not have to remember all of the names but Fig.2.8 is labelled for reference.

18. Study Fig.2.8 and then list the main long, short, flat and irregular bones of the human skeleton.

The skeleton can be divided into two systems, the *axial* and the *appendicular*. The axial skeleton forms the 'axis' of the body, and consists of the skull, vertebral column, sternum and rib cage. The appendicular skeleton consists of the two limb

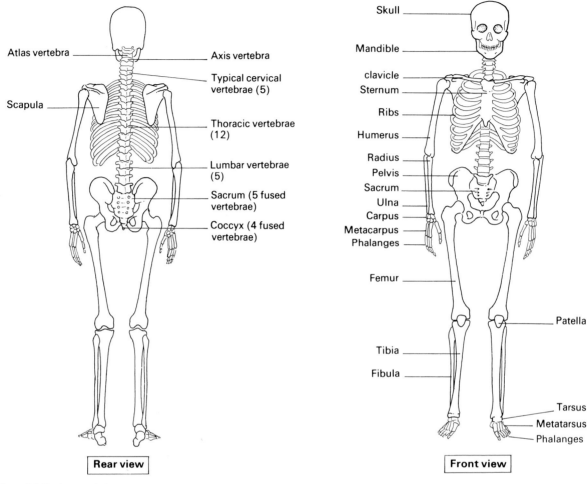

Labels (Rear view):
- Atlas vertebra
- Scapula
- Axis vertebra
- Typical cervical vertebrae (5)
- Thoracic vertebrae (12)
- Lumbar vertebrae (5)
- Sacrum (5 fused vertebrae)
- Coccyx (4 fused vertebrae)

Rear view

Labels (Front view):
- Skull
- Mandible
- clavicle
- Sternum
- Ribs
- Humerus
- Radius
- Pelvis
- Sacrum
- Ulna
- Carpus
- Metacarpus
- Phalanges
- Femur
- Patella
- Tibia
- Fibula
- Tarsus
- Metatarsus
- Phalanges

Front view

Figure 2.8 The human skeleton

girdles and the limbs, i.e. the pectoral girdle, to which the arms (forelimbs) are attached, and the pelvic girdle, to which the legs (hindlimbs) are attached.

The bones of the skeleton may also be classified as *cartilage bones* or *dermal bones* according to their origin. Most bones are pre-formed in cartilage, which then turns into bone (*ossifies*) following a definite time sequence. The bones of the cranium are different however. They form directly as bone in the dermal layer of the skin. Such bones are referred to as *dermal bones.*

Q 19. When a baby is born, the growth of the dermal bones of its cranium is incomplete. Can you think of an advantage and a disadvantage of this?

■ Joints

The points where adjacent bones meet are called *joints*. In many areas of the body, the bones are fused, and the joint is rigid and immovable. The bones of the cranium 'knit' together in *suture joints*, so producing a rigid protective 'brainbox'. In the pelvic girdle, the pubis, ilium and ischium are fused together making the so-called innominate bone, and the five sacral vertebrae are fused making the sacrum. These fusions result in an extremely strong structure, able to protect internal tissues and also to bear the weight of the body above it.

Other joints between bones are movable and are called *synovial joints* because they are lubricated with synovial fluid. Synovial joints are classified according to how much movement they permit:

• *hinge joints* allow only flexion and extension, e.g. elbow and knee
• *ball and socket joints* allow flexion, extension, abduction (away from mid-line), adduction (towards mid-line), and rotation, e.g. shoulder and hip
• *pivot joints* allow rotation, e.g. joint between atlas and axis bones at the top of the vertebral column
• *gliding joints* allow limited movement as two flattened surfaces glide over one another, e.g. joints between carpals in the wrist, and between tarsals in the ankle.

A synovial joint (Fig.2.9) is essentially a fluid-filled lubricating sac bound by the synovial membrane. The joint is strengthened and protected by the tough collagen, *joint capsule*, that surrounds the membrane, and this capsule is tightly anchored into each bone. The joint capsule may contain supporting *ligaments*, which are bundles of parallel elastic fibres that join bone to bone along lines of stress. The bone surfaces within the joint (*articular surfaces*) are covered with pads of *hyaline cartilage* so the bone surface does not wear away due to friction. The incompressability and resilience of cartilage also helps to give a measure of 'springiness' to the joint. This is particularly important in the knee joints during running. The synovial fluid is secreted by the highly *vascular* synovial membrane. It is made thick and viscous for its lubricating function by the presence of high concentrations of GAGs (see page 29), and it also performs the function of tissue fluid for the joint tissues. Some cells in the synovial fluid are phagocytic. This means that they can engulf any debris that arises in the joint fluid, and are essential for the smooth functioning of the joint. Only enough synovial fluid is present in the joint to form a film over those surfaces that require lubrication. The knee joint contains approximately 3.0 cm^3 of synovial fluid.

■ Bipedalism

Humans are bipedal, i.e. they walk upright on two legs. The long bones of the hind limbs (femur, tibia and fibula) have become longer than in human ancestors and cousins (e.g. apes), and the shape of the pelvis has been modified so that the centre of gravity lies vertically above the legs. The big toe is no longer opposable (capable of being placed with the front surface opposite) to the next toe as it is in apes, but provides a larger foot surface on the ground for greater stability. Instead of being flat, the foot is developed into an arch-like structure with a well-developed heel, allowing us to walk on tiptoe with a spring. Our stride involves both the heel and ball of each foot; in contrast an 'ape walk' would be like trying to walk on one's heels only.

Becoming bipedal was a major step in human evolution. It freed the forelimbs to do other things and made possible the development of the hand, manual dexterity, tool-making and so on. It also brought the face into a more prominent position, in particular allowing both the eyes and the mouth to face forward. This was essential in the development of communication, both by facial gestures and by speech. Together with the development of the brain, bipedalism has led to all of our achievements to date.

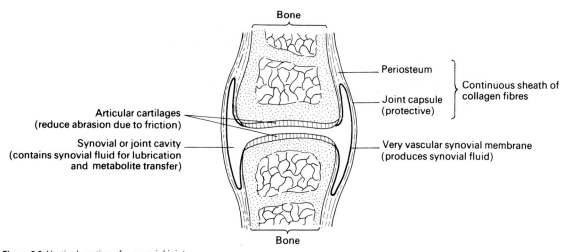

Figure 2.9 Vertical section of a synovial joint

3 TRANSPORT SYSTEMS

■ CASE STUDY: HEART SURGERY

Many hospitals produce leaflets like the one below to give to patients who require heart surgery. If such patients understand how their heart works and the nature of their problem, they may face their operation with greater confidence.

A NEW START FOR YOU AND YOUR HEART

BRITISH HEART FOUNDATION
The heart research charity
14 Fitzhardinge Street, London W1H 4DH
Reprinted 1989

WHY DO I NEED HEART SURGERY?
The decision to advise heart surgery in your case has been taken after detailed tests showed an abnormality in your heart for which surgery is considered the best and safest treatment. There are two main reasons for advising heart surgery: one is for disease of the coronary arteries, the other is for disease of the valves of the heart.

Q 1. Do you think that all prospective heart surgery patients should be given this information?

■ THE STRUCTURE AND MECHANICS OF THE HEART

Study Figs.3.1 and 3.2(a) and (b) which show the structure of the heart. The structure is closely related to the function of the heart, which is to pump the entire blood volume round the body in continual motion throughout life. The blood volume may vary under certain circumstances, but it averages 60 cm^3 per kg body mass.

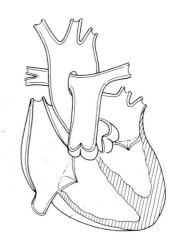

Figure 3.1 The internal structure of the heart

Q 2. Explain why the wall of the left ventricle is thicker than the right. Work out the precise function of the valves shown in Fig.3.2(b).

3. Calculate the blood volume (in dm^3) of a human who weighs 100 kg. Now calculate your own blood volume.

4. The volume of blood pumped out of the heart each minute is the cardiac output. This will also vary according to circumstances but averages six litres per minute (nearly ten pints!). Calculate the average volume of blood pumped out by the heart in a day.

5. What circumstances might cause this cardiac output to increase?

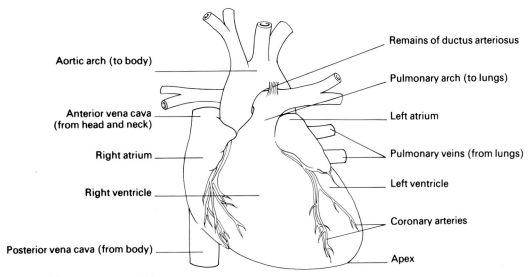

Aortic arch (to body)

Anterior vena cava (from head and neck)

Right atrium

Right ventricle

Posterior vena cava (from body)

Remains of ductus arteriosus

Pulmonary arch (to lungs)

Left atrium

Pulmonary veins (from lungs)

Left ventricle

Coronary arteries

Apex

Figure 3.2 (a) External features of the heart

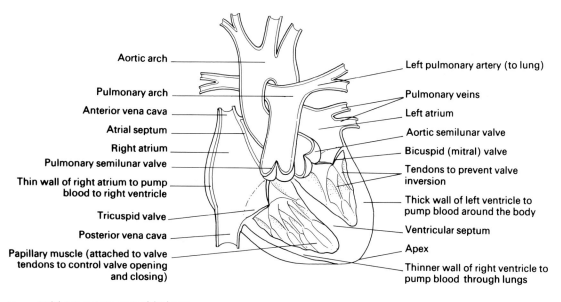

Aortic arch

Pulmonary arch

Anterior vena cava

Atrial septum

Right atrium

Pulmonary semilunar valve

Thin wall of right atrium to pump blood to right ventricle

Tricuspid valve

Posterior vena cava

Papillary muscle (attached to valve tendons to control valve opening and closing)

Left pulmonary artery (to lung)

Pulmonary veins

Left atrium

Aortic semilunar valve

Bicuspid (mitral) valve

Tendons to prevent valve inversion

Thick wall of left ventricle to pump blood around the body

Ventricular septum

Apex

Thinner wall of right ventricle to pump blood through lungs

Figure 3.2 (b) Internal structure of the heart

■ Double pump

A characteristic of mammals is that they have a *double circulation*; the pulmonary circulation taking blood to and from the lungs, and the systemic circulation serving the rest of the body. The heart is therefore a double pump in which the two sides are completely separated by a wall (*septum*). The right side pumps mainly *deoxygenated* blood to the lungs for gas exchange with the alveolar air, while the left side pumps mainly *oxygenated* blood

around the body for gas exchange with the tissues.

The cardiac output vessels are the aortic arch from the left ventricle which leads to arteries supplying the body, and the pulmonary arch from the right ventricle which leads to the pulmonary arteries.

The venous return vessels are the pulmonary veins from the lungs to the left atrium, and the venae cavae from the body tissues to the right atrium.

■ Heart valves

There are *valves* in the heart and in the veins to maintain a linear flow of blood, i.e. in one direction only. *Semilunar* valves occur in the bases of the aortic and pulmonary arches, and *atrioventricular* valves separate each atrium and ventricle, with the *tricuspid* valve between the two right chambers, and the *bicuspid* (*mitral*) valve between the left chambers. The atrioventricular valves are held in place by tendons (chordae tendineae or 'heart strings') and are regulated by the *papillary muscles* of the ventricle wall to which the tendons are attached. It is the slamming shut of these heart valves that results in the characteristic 'lub-dup' sound that the doctor hears when listening to the heartbeat.

Q 6. As a result of an illness such as rheumatic fever, the heart valves may become damaged and will not fully open or close. If this happened to the mitral valve, what do you think would be the effects on the circulation?

■ Cardiac cycle

The pumping activity of the heart is described by the cardiac cycle. One cardiac cycle consists of systole, which is when the heart is contracting, following by diastole, which is when the heart is relaxing (Fig.3.3) Although the two ventricles contract simultaneously from the apex upwards, the atria contract slightly ahead of them, with the right atrium contracting slightly earlier than the left. Together with the valves this staggering of contractions ensures a linear flow of blood, which would not be the case if all parts of the heart contracted and relaxed simultaneously. As long as the heart is pumping effectively, there should be no damming of blood, and the cardiac output from the ventricles should equal the venous return to the atria.

The stages in the cardiac cycle are as follows:
• The venous return of deoxygenated blood from the body enters the relaxing right atrium via the venae cavae; the venous return of oxygenated blood from the lungs enters the left atrium via the

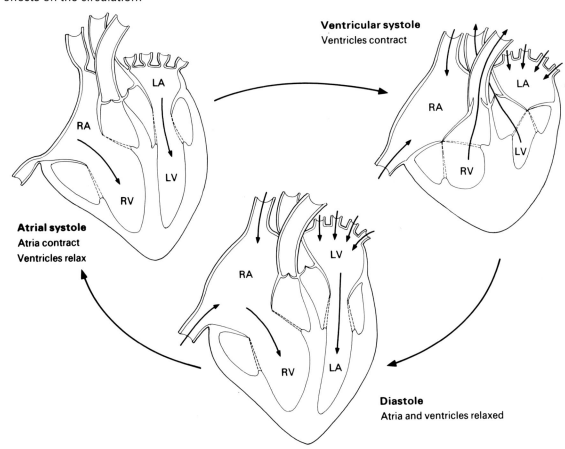

Figure 3.3 The heart at different stages in the cardiac cycle

pulmonary veins. At this stage some blood will also pass into the relaxed ventricles. When the atria contract, valves in the veins prevent the backflow of blood.

• When the atria are full, their walls contract, pushing blood through the open mitral valve and tricuspid valves into the relaxed ventricles (atrial systole).

• After a slight delay, the ventricles contract from the apex upwards, forcing the blood at high pressure through the semilunar valves into the arches (ventricular systole). This pressure causes the mitral and tricuspid valves to slam shut, thus preventing backflow of blood to the atria. This also means that while the ventricles are emptying, the atria can start to fill up again with blood.

• When the ventricles relax (diastole), the sudden drop in pressure causes the aortic and pulmonary valves to slam shut, so preventing backflow of blood from the arches.

■ Cardiac muscle

The walls of the heart are composed of *cardiac muscle*, and their thickness is closely related to the pumping load of each chamber. Thus the atria have thin walls as they only have to pump blood to the ventricles, the right ventricle has a moderately thick wall to enable it to pump blood round the pulmonary circulation, while the left ventricle has the thickest wall because it has to pump blood all the way round the body.

Cardiac muscle has a superb blood supply of its own, called the *coronary circulation*. This ensures that the muscle receives sufficient oxygen and nutrients for its continual functioning, and that waste products are removed efficiently. Remember that life itself depends on the continued efficiency of cardiac muscle and its blood supply, with your heart beating on average 72 times every minute that you are alive.

Q 7. How many times must your heart beat in a year, and how many times in a lifetime (say of 70 years)?

Before studying the next section, read again the section on striated muscle (page 21.)

Look at Fig.3.4. As in striated muscle, there are many *mitochondria* present in cardiac muscle. The contractile proteins of cardiac muscle are also organised into sarcomeres, fibrils and fibres, but here the fibres are composed of short, often

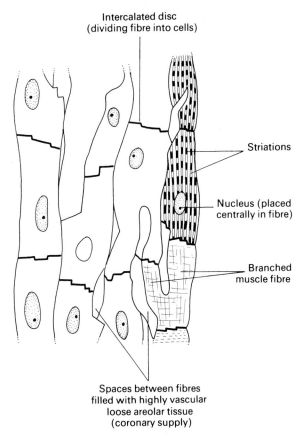

Figure 3.4 The histology of cardiac muscle

branched, individual cells with elaborate junctions between them. These junctions appear as lines under the light microscope and are referred to as *intercalated discs*. Under the electron microscope, the discs are seen to be highly-folded adjacent cell membranes, with areas of adhesion (*intermediate junctions*) and desmosomes holding them firmly together. There are also *gap junctions* in the membranes which allow rapid ion transport from cell to cell, so permitting waves of depolarisation (contraction) and repolarisation (relaxation) to pass along the fibres.

Since the cardiac muscle is arranged as a 'basin-like' mass of tissue around each heart chamber, shortening of the cells and fibres results in a decreased chamber volume, so blood is forced onwards.

Q 8. What are gap junctions, intermediate junctions and desmosomes? (If you do not know, refer to page 6.)

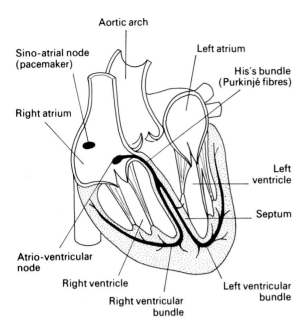

Figure 3.5 The conducting system of the heart (vertical section)

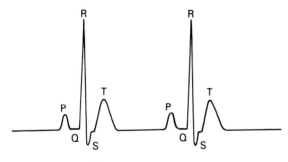

P wave = atrial depolarisation
QRS complex = ventricular depolarisation
T wave = ventricular repolarisation
P–Q distance ≡ delay in passing atrio-ventricular node
and His's bundle

Figure 3.6 A normal ECG trace

Cardiac muscle is *myogenic*, meaning that it can contract and relax regularly of its own accord without external nervous stimulation. As the cells are linked by gap junctions which allow ion exchange, the contraction of one cell stimulates the contraction of other cells at either end. This means that the cell with the fastest rate of spontaneous contraction will impose its rate on the surrounding cells.

The region of the heart that has the fastest inherent rhythm is called the *sino-atrial node* (*pacemaker*) situated in the wall of the right atrium. This initiates waves of depolarisation (causing contraction) which spread first through the wall of the right atrium, and then through the wall of the left atrium; which is why the right atrium contracts before the left one. The waves of depolarisation then reach the *atrioventricular node* at the top of the ventricular septum. This node causes a slight delay in the passage of the impulses before they are passed rapidly to the apex of the heart through the *Purkinjé fibres* of *His's bundle*. From here, waves of depolarisation pass through the cardiac muscle fibres of the ventricles, causing contraction to occur from the apex upwards. As the muscle fibres repolarise, they relax. The delay at the atrioventricular node means that ventricular contraction is delayed until after atrial contraction.

[Q] 9. What do you understand by the terms 'depolarisation' and 'repolarisation'? (Refer to the section on nerve impulses on page 81 if you don't know.)

■ ECG recording
The electrical activity of the heart can be recorded at the body surface using a sensitive device called an electrocardiograph machine. Impulses are displayed graphically as an electrocardiograph (ECG) which can give information about normal heart activity and also shows up any abnormalities in the cardiac rhythm (Fig.3.5). Slow heart rates can be corrected by a pacemaker implant .

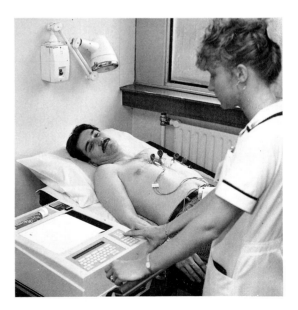

Recording an ECG

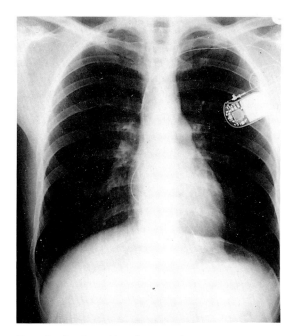

X-ray showing the position of a pacemaker

(a)

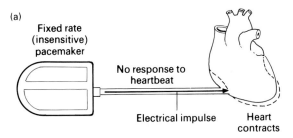

Fixed rate (insensitive) pacemaker

No response to heartbeat

Electrical impulse

Heart contracts

(b)

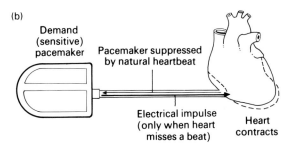

Demand (sensitive) pacemaker

Pacemaker suppressed by natural heartbeat

Electrical impulse (only when heart misses a beat)

Heart contracts

Figure 3.6 Each year about 7000 patients in Great Britain have an electronic pacemaker (pulse generator) surgically implanted, usually in the muscle of the chest. These matchbox size devices are used to correct slow heart rates caused by disease and ageing of the heart. The modern pacemakers are powered by lithium batteries and have a life of ten to twelve years. Some types deliver a regular impulse (Fig 3.6(a)) say sixty times a minute, causing the heart to beat at a steady rate. Others are sensitive to the actual heartbeat (Fig. 3.6(b)) and only deliver an impulse when needed (From British Heart Foundation Leaflet no. 9, *Pacemakers.*)

Q 10. If part of the ventricular septum is damaged, as for example in partial heart block, the passage of impulses through His's bundle will be slowed. How might this alter the appearance of the ECG?

■ Ultrasound scanning

The heart may also be visualised as a moving object using ultrasound. This is high frequency sound (1-5 MHz) which can be directed as short, sharp pulses into the body. The echoes that are reflected off body organs are detected by the scanner, and changed (*transduced*) into pictures on a screen or photograph. An ultrasound of the heart can be seen in Fig.3.7. By scanning the heart, it is possible to observe defective valve movements or wall movements.

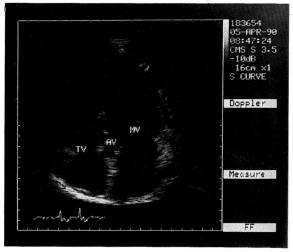

Ultrasound scan of heart valves

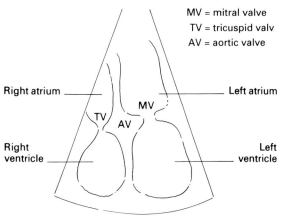

MV = mitral valve
TV = tricuspid valv
AV = aortic valve

Right atrium

Left atrium

MV

TV AV

Right ventricle

Left ventricle

Figure 3.7 Diagrammatic representation of the scan above

■ Corrective heart surgery

Damage to heart muscle is most likely to be due to accumulations of fat blocking the coronary arteries, so reducing the blood supply to the muscle fibres (Fig.3.8(a)). The starved muscle fibres initially cause pain, called angina, and then eventually cease to function altogether. If the damage is not too extensive the blockage can be bypassed surgically with a coronary bypass operation, in which a section of vein from the patient's leg is stitched onto the heart (Fig.3.7(b)). This provides a new pathway for blood to reach the muscle, which should then repair. For a patient with widespread heart disease however, a heart transplant may be the only solution. As with other organ transplants, this requires a suitable donor heart which closely matches the patient's tissue type. If the antigenic cell membrane proteins on the donor organ are too different, the patient will manufacture antibodies against them and the transplanted heart will be rejected.

(a)

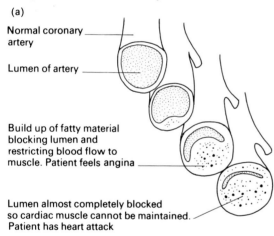

Normal coronary artery

Lumen of artery

Build up of fatty material blocking lumen and restricting blood flow to muscle. Patient feels angina

Lumen almost completely blocked so cardiac muscle cannot be maintained. Patient has heart attack

(b)

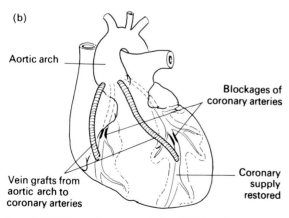

Aortic arch

Blockages of coronary arteries

Vein grafts from aortic arch to coronary arteries

Coronary supply restored

Figure 3.8 (a) Diseased coronary arteries. (b) Vein grafts to restore coronary supply

■ THE CONTROL OF HEART FUNCTION

So far we have considered the heart as an isolated organ, but it is of course an integral part of the whole body. The cardiac output must be modified to meet the varying needs of the body, so although cardiac contraction is initiated internally, an external control system is also required. This is achieved by the autonomic nervous system, and by *negative feedback* control mechanisms. In negative feedback a stimulus initiates actions which reverse or reduce the stimulus (see Chapter 7 page 79). The nerves to the heart can be seen in Fig.3.9.

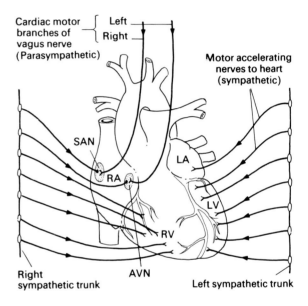

Cardiac motor branches of vagus nerve (Parasympathetic)

Left
Right

Motor accelerating nerves to heart (sympathetic)

SAN

LA

RA

LV

RV

Right sympathetic trunk

AVN

Left sympathetic trunk

Figure 3.9 Autonomic nerves to the heart

■ Cardiac control centres

There are two control centres for regulating the heart, and both occur in the *medulla* of the brain. The *cardioacceleratory centre (CAC)* is concerned with increasing cardiac output, while the *cardio-inhibitory centre (CIC)* reduces cardiac output.
• From the CAC, *sympathetic fibres* pass down the spinal cord and emerge in the sympathetic accelerator nerves to the sino-atrial node, atrio-ventricular node and cardiac muscle. When the centre is stimulated, impulses pass through the sympathetic nerves to the heart where *noradrenaline* is released at the neuromuscular junctions. This increases the rate of the heartbeat by stimulating the sino-atrial node and reducing the delay at the atrioventricular node. It also increases the force of the muscle contractions.

• From the CIC, *parasympathetic fibres* reach the sino-atrial node and atrioventricular node via the *vagus nerves* (the tenth cranial nerve). When the centre is stimulated, nerve impulses pass to the heart nodes where *acetylcholine* is relesased. This slows the heartbeat rate by suppressing the sino-atrial node and increasing the delay at the atrioventricular node.

Q 11. What happens to the following when cardiac output increases: (a) the venous return, (b) the stretchability of cardiac muscle fibres, (c) the arterial blood pressure, (d) the venous blood pressure?

■ How are the cardiac centres stimulated or inhibited?

Stimulation or inhibition of the cardiac control centres may occur by three separate reflex pathways:
• The *carotid sinus reflex* is concerned with maintaining the correct blood supply to the brain. The carotid sinus is a swelling at the base of the carotid artery to the brain, in the wall of which are *baroreceptors* (pressure receptors). If the blood pressure rises, the carotid sinus wall is stretched and the baroreceptors fire off impulses to the cardioinhibitory centre. Cardiac output is reduced so blood pressure falls. As the sinus wall becomes less stretched, the baroreceptors are no longer stimulated, and the cardioacceleratory centre now dominates. Thus cardiac output increases and so does the blood pressure.
• The *aortic reflex* operates in the same way as the carotid reflex but is concerned with the general systemic blood pressure. It is initiated by baroreceptors in the aortic arch.
• The *Bainbridge reflex* regulates venous pressure. If this pressure rises, baroreceptors in the walls of the venae cavae and right atrium fire off impulses to the CAC, thus increasing cardiac output.

Q 12. Beta-blockers are drugs which inhibit the sympathetic nerves to the heart. Will they raise or lower blood pressure?

13. If you jump up suddenly from lying down, the effect of gravity could cause the blood pressure in your brain to drop suddenly, making you faint. Why doesn't this normally happen?

14. What effect would changing blood volume due to changing water content have on blood pressure?

15. The volume of blood pumped out of the heart in one beat is called the *stroke volume*, and can be calculated from the heart rate and the cardiac output. For example, if the heart rate is 75 beats per minute, and cardiac output is 5.25 dm^3 per minute, then the stroke volume is 70 cm^3 (i.e. 75 beats x 70 cm^3 = 5.25 dm^3). Now calculate the stroke volume during hard physical exertion, when the heart rate is 120 beats per minute, and cardiac output is 15.6 dm^3 per minute. What effect would this have on blood pressure?

■ THE CIRCULATION

Mammals have a complete or *closed* blood system. This means that blood is always contained within blood vessels, circulating the body in arteries, capillaries and veins (Fig.3.10).

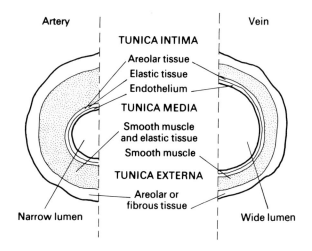

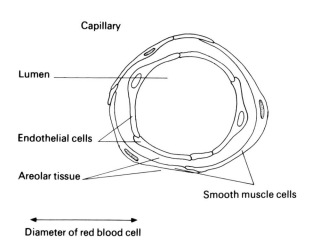

Figure 3.10 Structure of blood vessels (transverse section)

The walls of an artery and a vein have the same basic structure, being composed of an inner lining (*endothelium*) of simple squamous epithelial cells, a layer of *elastic* tissue and *smooth muscle* tissue of varying thickness, and an outer *fibrous coat*. The capillary wall consists only of the inner endothelium, and one or two smooth muscle cells.

■ Arteries

Arteries carry blood at high pressure *away from* the heart, and must therefore be able to withstand surges of pressure and flow related to the heartbeat. Such pressure is greatest at ventricular systole, which can be felt as a *pulse* in arteries that are close to the body surface. The artery wall contains elastic fibres throughout its thickness to help accommodate pressure changes. At systole, this tissue allows expansion of the artery to contain the increased blood volume, and at diastole, its elastic recoil helps to push the blood onwards. There is a greater proportion of elastic tissue to muscle tissue in the larger arteries such as the aorta where pressure is greatest. The *smooth muscle tissue* of artery walls contains both longitudinal and circular fibres, and is important in giving arteries their ability to contract. The muscle cells are under sympathetic nervous control, and when stimulated to contract they squeeze the artery cavity (*lumen*) resulting in *vasoconstriction*. When sympathetic stimulation is removed or inhibited, the smooth muscle cells relax and the lumen widens again (*vasodilation*). Smaller arteries (*arterioles*) have a greater proportion of muscle tissue to elastic tissue in their walls making them more effective at vasoconstriction and dilation. This property allows the blood flow to different parts of the body to be varied according to its needs.

The outer *fibrous coat* of the artery wall contains *collagen* fibres. These have considerable tensile strength and help to prevent the rupturing of the artery under high internal pressure. Arterioles deliver blood to the capillaries. As the arterioles decrease in size, their histology changes and grades into that of capillaries.

■ Capillaries

Capillaries are microscopic blood vessels that link arterioles to their equivalent - the *venules*. They occur close to most body cells, their density depending mainly on the activity of the tissue concerned. Thus active tissue such as that of muscles, liver, kidneys and endocrine glands have extensive capillary networks, while the less active

tendons and ligaments have fewer capillaries, and some tissues such as the epidermis, cornea and cartilage have no capillaries at all.

Capillaries are well suited to the function of exchange of metabolites between the blood and the tissue cells. Their extensive branching networks serve to increase the surface area for exchange, and the single layer of endothelial cells in their wall presents a minimal barrier. To aid exchange many capillaries also have small windows (*fenestrations*) in their walls, where endothelial cytoplasm is missing. These fenestrations are closed by the basement membrane (see page 9) of the endothelium which is continuous across the gaps.

Q 16. Why do you think fenestrated capillaries are abundant in the following: (a) villi, (b) glomeruli, (c) the thyroid gland?

■ Sinusoids

Sinusoids are microscopic blood vessels that occur in certain organs of the body such as the liver, spleen, adrenal cortex, pituitary and thymus. They are wider than capillaries, and their walls contain phagocytic cells amongst the squamous epithelium (e.g. Kupffer cells in the liver sinusoids). These phagocytic cells ingest bacteria that are present in the blood. (See the section on defence against disease, page 17.) Like capillaries, sinusoids eventually join to form venules.

■ Veins

Veins carry blood *towards* the heart and tend to have a wider lumen and thinner walls than arteries. Compared with an artery, the wall of a vein contains less elastic tissue, less smooth muscle and more collagen fibres. It retains enough elasticity to withstand pressure and volume changes in the passing blood, but the pressure is lower than in arteries, and the pulse has been reduced by the capillaries. Despite the assistance of external pressure surrounding skeletal muscles, the propelling pressure in the limb veins and others is barely enough to overcome gravity. *Valves* are therefore present to prevent the backflow of blood.

Under certain circumstances these valves may become weak and fail to operate efficiently. Backflow may therefore occur, with accumulated blood causing the wall of the vein below the failed valve to become stretched and pouched out. Such veins are said to be *varicose*, and are common in the legs and around the anus (where they are referred to as *haemorrhoids* or *piles*).

■ Blood flow through the circulation

Blood flows through a closed blood system because of different pressures in the component parts, always flowing from high to low pressure. The mean pressure values are shown in Table 3.1.

	kPa	mm Hg
Aorta	13.3	100
Arteries	5.3 - 13.3	40 - 100
Arterioles	3.3 - 5.3	25 - 40
Capillaries	1.6 - 3.3	12 - 25
Venules	1.1 - 1.6	8 - 12
Veins	0.7 - 1.1	5 - 8
Venae cavae	0.3 - 0.7	2 - 5
Right atrium	0 at diastole	0

Table 3.1 Mean blood pressure values

These blood pressures are mean values, and may in fact vary considerably under different circumstances. Factors affecting blood pressure include the cardiac output (see page 34), the blood volume, and the peripheral resistance of the vessels to blood flow.

• *Blood volume* and hence pressure may rise with a high dietary salt intake for example, as salt in the blood will tend to hold water osmotically. In contrast blood volume and pressure may fall in the case of haemorrhage or severe bleeding, when a blood transfusion may become necessary.

• *Peripheral resistance* occurs because of friction between the blood and the inner surface of the vessel walls, and any increased resistance will cause the blood pressure to rise. Resistance may increase, for example, if the blood becomes more viscous (i.e. less 'runny').

Q 17. What effects might a fall in blood pressure have on: (a) glomerular function in the kidney, (b) gas exchange in the alveoli, (c) the brain?

18. What effects might the following have on blood viscosity and hence on blood pressure: (a) dehydration, (b) an increased red cell count, (c) decreased plasma protein concentration?

19. Atherosclerosis is a condition that results from the deposition of fatty substances such as cholesterol in the walls of arteries. This may damage the endothelium allowing platelets to stick to the damaged wall. The platelets then cause the formation of a *plaque*, which is a swelling that protrudes into the lumen of the vessel.
(a) What effect would plaques have on blood pressure in the vessel?
(b) What may happen if plaques develop in the coronary arteries?
(c) If a blood clot (*thrombus*) breaks off from the surface of the plaque, what might be the serious outcome?
(d) What sort of diet might lead to atherosclerosis?

■ Control of blood pressure in the circulation

We have already seen how blood pressure can be controlled by the CAC and the CIC adjusting cardiac output (see page 40). The medulla of the brain also contains a group of neurones, called the *vasomotor centre*, which regulates the diameter of the arterioles. Impulses are continually transmitted along sympathetic fibres to the smooth muscle of arteriole walls so that a moderate amount of contraction is present all the time. If the frequency of impulses is increased, vasoconstriction results, and similarly, a decreased impulse frequency leads to vasodilation.

Like the CAC and CIC, the vasomotor centre receives information from pressure receptors in the carotid and aortic sinuses. A fall in blood pressure causes the receptors to send impulses to the vasomotor centre to increase the sympathetic stimulation of the arteriole walls and thus blood pressure rises.

The vasomotor centre also receives information from *chemoreceptors* in the carotid and aortic sinuses. A rise in the carbon dioxide level in the blood, a fall in the oxygen level, or a fall in the hydrogen ion concentration, will all stimulate the chemoreceptors to send impulses to the vasomotor centre. The resulting vasoconstriction has the effect of increasing blood flow through the lungs for greater gas exchange. At the same time the carotid and aortic chemoreceptors will also have triggered an increase in the frequency and depth of breathing movements (see page 55).

Blood pressure and flow in the circulation may be affected by certain chemicals, an example being adrenaline, secreted by the adrenal medulla in times of stress. Adrenaline causes an increase in cardiac output and hence blood pressure, and effectively diverts blood to where it is needed, causing vasoconstriction of arterioles to the skin and gut, and vasodilation of arterioles to the brain and skeletal muscles. (See page 99 for more information about adrenaline.)

■ The circulatory pathway

A good way to learn the 'geography' of the circulation is to trace the route taken by a red cell from organ to organ. For example, to get from the brain to the lungs the red cell would take the following pathway: capillary of brain - venule - internal jugular vein - subclavian vein - brachiocephalic vein - superior vena cava - right atrium - tricuspid valve - right ventricle - pulmonary semilunar valve - pulmonary arch - pulmonary artery - arteriole - capillary of lungs.

Unlike other veins, the *hepatic portal vein* acts as a shunt vessel, transporting blood from the intestines direct to the liver.

Q 20. With the aid of Fig.3.11 outline the path of a red blood cell from the lungs to the liver, and from the liver back to the lungs.

21. Locate the point where the lymph drains from the lymphatic system into the blood system (see Figs.3.12 and 3.13).

22. Why do you think the hepatic portal vein is necessary, and how will its blood composition differ from that of the hepatic vein?

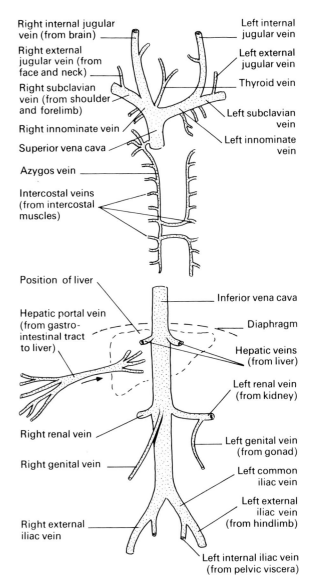

Right common carotid artery
Right subclavian artery
Innominate artery
Ascending thoracic aorta
Coronary arteries (to heart)
Left common carotid artery (to head and neck)
Left subclavian artery (to shoulder and forelimb)
Descending thoracic aorta
Intercostal arteries (to intercostal muscles)
Phrenic arteries (to diaphragm)
Position of diaphragm
Coeliac axis
Gastric artery (to stomach)
Splenic artery (to spleen)
Hepatic artery (to liver)
Renal arteries (to kidneys)
Abdominal aorta
Genital arteries (to ovaries or testes)
Superior mesenteric artery (to intestines)
Posterior mesenteric artery (to rectum)
Right common iliac artery
Internal iliac arteries (to bladder and uterus)
Right external iliac artery (to hind limb)
Left common iliac artery

Figure 3.11 (a) The aorta and its branches

Right internal jugular vein (from brain)
Right external jugular vein (from face and neck)
Right subclavian vein (from shoulder and forelimb)
Right innominate vein
Superior vena cava
Azygos vein
Intercostal veins (from intercostal muscles)
Left internal jugular vein
Left external jugular vein
Thyroid vein
Left subclavian vein
Left innominate vein
Position of liver
Hepatic portal vein (from gastro-intestinal tract to liver)
Inferior vena cava
Diaphragm
Hepatic veins (from liver)
Left renal vein (from kidney)
Right renal vein
Right genital vein
Left genital vein (from gonad)
Left common iliac vein
Left external iliac vein (from hindlimb)
Right external iliac vein
Left internal iliac vein (from pelvic viscera)

Figure 3.11 (b) The main veins in the body.
(It is unlikely you will have to learn all of these names!)

THE LYMPHATIC TRANSPORT SYSTEM

CASE STUDY: SWOLLEN ANKLES ON THE MENU?

Mrs Morris works in the school canteen and stands in one position for several hours each day. Her legs and ankles have swollen, not with blood, but with an accumulation of intercellular tissue fluid because her lymph is not being returned to the blood system effectively. The doctor prescribed a diuretic drug to make her lose more water in her urine. This would reduce her blood volume and hence blood pressure and so reduce the amount of tissue fluid being formed. More later...

Formation of tissue fluid

Tissue fluid, or intercellular fluid, is derived from blood plasma but contains none of the plasma proteins. It is formed at the arterial end of the capillary bed, and carries oxygen, glucose, amino acids and other metabolites from the blood to the tissues. After exchange, much of the waste fluid (now called *lymph*) drains away in the lymph vessels. Study Fig.3.12. There are four pressures operating between the blood and the tissues:

• *Blood pressure* averages 3.3 kPa at the arterial end of the capillaries and 1.3 kPa at the venous end. This pressure will act to push water and small molecules out of the capillaries by *ultrafiltration* (filtration under pressure).

• *Intercellular fluid pressure* averages –0.8 kPa, (negative as it is less than atmospheric pressure) and acts to push water and small molecules back into the capillaries. The net filtration pressure is therefore 3.3–(–0.8) kPa = 4.1 kPa at the arterial end and 1.3–(–0.8) kPa = 2.1 kPa at the venous end.

• *Osmotic pressure of plasma proteins* in the blood averages 3.7 kPa. This pressure acts to draw water back into the capillaries.

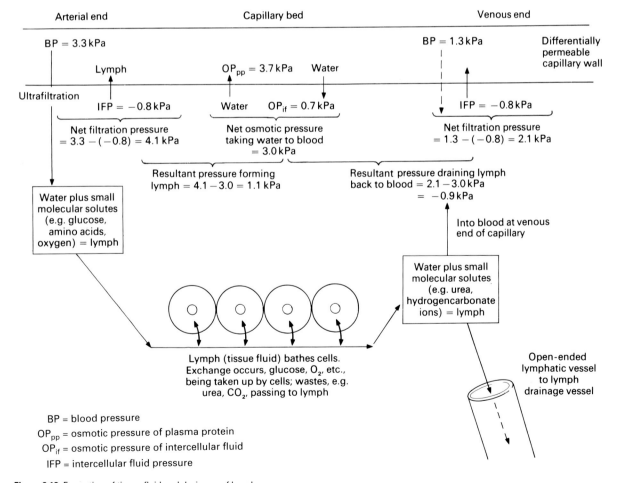

BP = blood pressure
OP$_{pp}$ = osmotic pressure of plasma protein
OP$_{if}$ = osmotic pressure of intercellular fluid
IFP = intercellular fluid pressure

Figure 3.12 Formation of tissue fluid and drainage of lymph

• *Osmotic pressure of solutes* in the intercellular fluid averages 0.7 kPa, and acts in the reverse direction, drawing water out of the capillaries. The net osmotic force at both ends of the capillary bed is therefore 3.7–0.7 = 3.0 kPa.

The resultant total pressure at the arterial end is 4.1–3.0 = +1.1 kPa, a positive pressure that will tend to force fluid out of the capillaries and so form the tissue fluid (lymph).

The resultant pressure at the venous end is 2.1–3.0 = –0.9 kPa, a negative pressure that will draw fluid back into the capillaries after exchange. As this pressure is lower than the arterial pressure, some fluid must also drain into the lymphatic vessels.

■ Drainage of lymph

The lymph vessels are open-ended in the tissues, and lymph containing carbon dioxide, nitrogenous waste and other excretory products is drawn into them. It then passes through the lymphatic vessels, and is eventually returned to the bloodstream when the *thoracic lymph duct* empties into the left *subclavian vein* in the neck. Lymphatic vessels have a similar structure to veins, with *valves* to prevent backflow of fluid, but the only propulsive force comes from the pressure on the lymph vessels of surrounding muscles as they contract and relax. The lymphatic vessels are illustrated in Fig.3.13.

Q 23. Returning to Mrs Morris (page 45), can you now: (a) explain why her problem was caused by tissue fluid and not blood as she thought, (b) suggest an alternative treatment the doctor could have recommended without the use of drugs?

■ Lymph nodes

At particular locations along the lymph ducts there are lymph nodes. These are made up of a reservoir of B and T-lymphocytes for the immune response, and sinusoids through which the lymph percolates. Like the sinusoids in the liver, they contain phagocytic cells that ingest bacteria and other waste material in the lymph. The lymph nodes act in defence by preventing bacteria from entering the blood circulation from the tissue fluid. The lymph glands in the neck, groin or armpit (groups of nodes) become swollen in the event of bacterial infection.

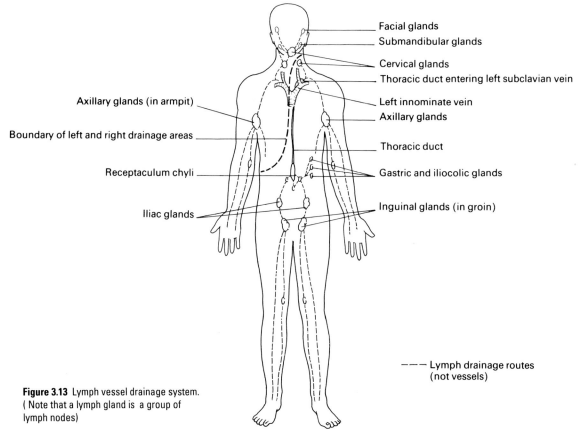

Facial glands
Submandibular glands
Cervical glands
Thoracic duct entering left subclavian vein
Left innominate vein
Axillary glands
Thoracic duct
Gastric and iliocolic glands
Inguinal glands (in groin)

Axillary glands (in armpit)
Boundary of left and right drainage areas
Receptaculum chyli
Iliac glands

– – – Lymph drainage routes (not vessels)

Figure 3.13 Lymph vessel drainage system. (Note that a lymph gland is a group of lymph nodes)

CHAPTER 4
BREATHING SYSTEMS

■ CASE STUDY: AN UNHEALTHY HABIT

Mr Riley noticed the 'No Smoking' sign in the surgery waiting room just in time. He cleared his throat awkwardly and slipped the cigarettes back into his pocket, hoping that he wouldn't have to wait much longer. He only smoked an average of ten cigarettes per day, but liked a few more when he was nervous or not too well. This cough lasted for two to three months every winter, but it seemed a lot worse this year. His chest really hurt, and the thick greenish sputum was harder to shift than usual.

At last it was his turn. The doctor listened to his chest, asked a few questions, and then diagnosed bronchitis. She explained that bronchitis is a chronic, or long-lasting, inflammation of the bronchial tree surfaces, caused by continual irritation - the commonest irritant being cigarette smoke. Once the surfaces were inflamed, they became increasingly susceptible to secondary infection, and this is why the discharge was thick and green. Mr Riley was given a course of *antibiotics* to stop the infection and told that he must give up smoking.

He did try for a few days, but once the antibiotics had had time to work, his chest felt clearer, and he persuaded himself that it was all a lot of scaremongering. He carried on smoking, and three years later died from **emphysema**. The irritation had caused considerable loss of elastic tissue from his lungs. This meant that large volumes of his lungs were not ventilating properly, so his blood stream was not being fully on-loaded with oxygen or fully off-loaded of carbon dioxide. Much of his respiratory surface (*alveolar surface*) had also been destroyed, and gaseous exchange between the air and his blood became insufficient to maintain life.

emphysema a swelling or inflation of the air passages of the lungs (due to the loss of elasticity), particularly in the alveoli. It is brought on by continual irritation and infection and is a frequent cause of death, especially in smokers

■ RESPIRATORY SURFACES

The respiratory surface is the surface across which the respiratory gases are exchanged, i.e. oxygen enters the blood and carbon dioxide leaves. Respiratory surfaces throughout the animal kingdom have a number of properties in common:
• the surface must be moist so that gases dissolve and rapid diffusion can occur
• the surface must also be thin, so that the diffusion distance is small
• the surface area must be large enough to cope with the amount of gaseous exchange needed by the animal, even under severe work loads. This surface area must also be kept clean to operate effectively
• the surface must have a very good blood supply so that there is efficient exchange between blood and air (or water in aquatic animals)
• the surface must be capable of being ventilated with air (or water in aquatic species) so that the source of oxygen is renewed and the carbon dioxide waste expelled.

These properties were greatly impaired in Mr Riley's lungs; the loss in function being aggravated by his continual smoking.

The respiratory surface in humans is in the lungs. It is ventilated by the mechanism of *breathing*, which involves the body system known as the *respiratory system*. (Note that we only use the term 'respiration' when describing the biochemical processes that release energy inside cells.)

■ THE HUMAN RESPIRATORY (BREATHING) SYSTEM

During this section refer to Figs. 4.1(a) and (b), and 4.2(a), (b), (c) and (d).

■ From nose to voice box
The nasal chamber is divided into left and right sides by a nasal septum made of cartilage. Air

enters through the two nostrils (*external nares*), passes over the *nasal mucosa*, and leaves the nasal cavity to the *pharynx* via two *internal nares*.

The nasal mucosa has a very large surface area and consists of a pseudostratified columnar epithelium (see page 9) which is mucus secreting and ciliated (to set up currents in the mucus). The epithelium layer is on the surface of areolar tissue which has a rich blood supply. As air passes over the nasal mucosa, it is *warmed*, *cleaned* and *moistened*. It is warmed by the blood flowing through the mucosa; cleaned as dust particles and bacteria become trapped in the mucus and are wafted to the nostrils by cilia beating, and moistened by the wet surfaces, so ensuring that the epithelia lining the *bronchial tree* and alveoli are not dried out (*desiccated*).

Towards the back of the nasal cavity, the nasal mucosa also has chemoreceptors for the perception of smells (olfactory sense). These cells can be depolarised when specific chemical substances dissolve in the mucus lining of that area of mucosa. Sometimes when we have a heavy cold we lose the ability to appreciate the flavour of food.

Q 1. Why are nosebleeds so common, and why can they often be controlled by placing ice packs on the neck?

The pharynx is the large chamber of the throat between the internal nostrils (internal nares) and the entrance to the larynx (*glottis*). It acts as a resonator to modify soundwaves during speech. During swallowing the glottis is covered by a flap (*epiglottis*) so that food does not pass down into the air passages. The voice box (*larnyx*) connects the glottis to the windpipe (*trachea*). The larynx is supported on the outside by plates of cartilage. Inside, its mucous membrane is folded to form the vocal cords, which vibrate as air passes through the larynx from the trachea when you breathe out. The sound waves formed in the air flow are the basis of speech. The shape of the buccal cavity, the tongue, and the teeth and lips all modify these basic sounds to allow for speech, song or screams!

■ The trachea

The trachea is the start of the *bronchial tree*, a system of tubes of decreasing diameter leading down to the alveoli of the lungs. The adult trachea is about 12 cm long and 2.5 cm in diameter after you breathe out, but its diameter and length

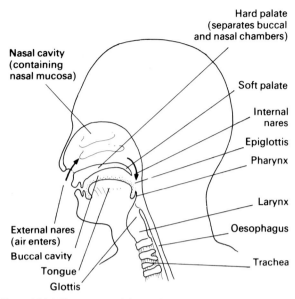

Figure 4.1 (a) The anatomy of the respiratory system in the head

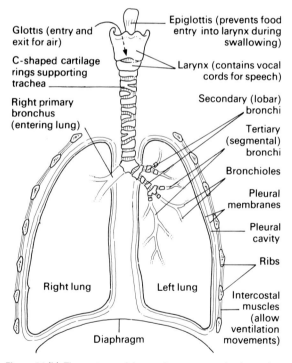

Figure 4.1 (b) The anatomy of the respiratory system in the neck and chest (ventral aspect, sectional view)

increases by as much as 20% when you breathe in. The structure of the trachea must therefore enable stretching, and must also be able to withstand the considerable air pressure variations that occur during ventilation movements.

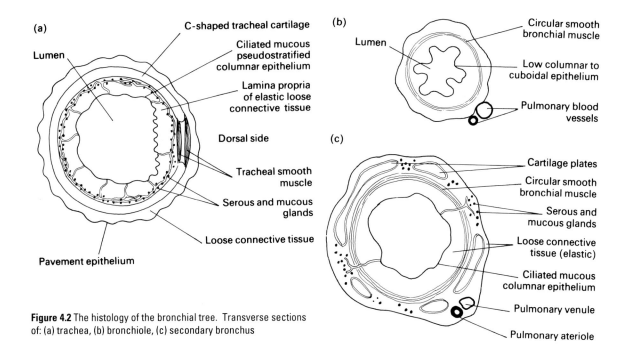

Figure 4.2 The histology of the bronchial tree. Transverse sections of: (a) trachea, (b) bronchiole, (c) secondary bronchus

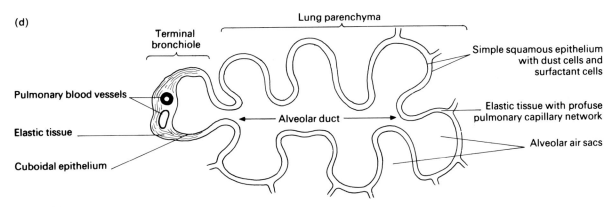

Figure 4.2 (d) Transverse section of the alveolar air sacs

Q 2. What pressure variations do you think will occur in the trachea during inspiration (breathing in) and expiration (breathing out)?

The wall of the trachea contains 16 to 20 *C-shaped rings of hyaline cartilage*. These allow changes in size and prevent the trachea from collapsing or ballooning due to pressure variations during breathing. They also ensure that the trachea is not obstructed when food passes down the adjacent foodpipe (*oesophagus*). Between the C-shaped cartilages are smooth muscles which adjust the air flow by changing the internal diameter of the trachea. The wall of the trachea contains elastic tissue, which reduces the expansion which occurs during ventilation. The internal epithelium is a mucous, ciliated, pseudostratified columnar epithelium (see page 10). It traps any dust in the air and wafts it up to the glottis. Here the mucus and debris pass into the oesophagus, are swallowed and then are disinfected in the acid of the stomach.

■ The bronchial tree

In the chest cavity (*thorax*), the trachea divides into the right and left primary *bronchi*, which enter the lungs. The bronchi then divide immediately into smaller tubes called *secondary* or *lobar bronchi*, which lead to the *lung lobes* (two in the left lung and three in the right). In the lobes, the lobar bronchi subdivide into *tertiary* or *segmental bronchi*, which themselves divide into *bronchioles* leading to the alveoli (Fig. 4.2). Lung tissue thus consists of alveolar air sacs and all the ducts of the bronchial tree.

Like the trachea, the bronchi and bronchioles possess elastic tissue in their walls to accommodate dimension changes. The primary bronchi resemble the trachea in all respects, but secondary and tertiary bronchi are supported by plates of hyaline cartilage rather than by C-shaped rings, and the epithelium is reduced to a mucous, ciliated, simple columnar type.

Bronchioles have no cartilage and only a simple columnar epithelium, without mucus-secreting goblet cells or cilia. This explains why people with chronic bronchitis, like Mr Riley often get lung infections, and may lose alveolar function and elasticity. Excessive mucus forms in the inflamed bronchi and seeps down towards the bronchioles and alveoli. With no cilia to remove the mucus, the tubes and air sacs can become blocked. This stagnant mucus is a prime target for bacterial infection.

The division of the bronchioles forms *terminal bronchioles* lined with cuboidal epithelium, which divide into *respiratory bronchioles* lined with squamous (pavement) epithelium (see page 8). These are the first parts of the *respiratory surface*, together with the alveolar ducts and alveolar air sacs. The squamous epithelium of the respiratory surface is very thin to minimise the diffusion distance between air and blood, and there is a profuse network of *pulmonary capillaries* just under the epithelium for efficient gas exchange. Oxygen dissolves in the moist lining of the alveoli and diffuses into the bloodstream, whilst the carbon dioxide diffuses out of the blood stream and into the alveolar air.

Some of the epithelial cells lining the alveoli are modified to form either *surfactant cells* or *dust cells*. Surfactant cells produce *phospholipids* which act as *surfactants*. These soapy substances reduce the surface tension of the tissue fluid on the huge alveolar surface area. Without these surfactants the lungs could not be inflated since the surface tension would be too great. Dust cells are free macrophages, which engulf dust particles in the alveoli and so attempt to keep the alveoli clean.

Q 3. In premature babies (those born before 36 weeks) inadequate surfactants are formed in the alveolar fluid. Why is this a problem for the baby, and what treatment is required until the surfactant cells are fully developed?

■ Gross lung structure

The lungs are two cone-shaped organs lying in the thoracic cavity, separated from one another by the heart (Fig.4.16). Two moist connective tissue membranes, called *pleural membranes*, enclose and protect each lung. The outer *parietal pleura* is coated with pavement epithelium (see page 8) and sticks strongly to the wall of the thorax. The inner *visceral pleura* is a similar structure but sticks strongly to the outer surface of the lungs. Between these membranes is the *pleural cavity* which contains a lubricating fluid secreted by both membranes. This fluid allows them to slide over each other without friction during breathing movements. There is a negative pressure (i.e. less than the air pressure in the lungs) in the pleural cavity which keeps the lungs expanded to the chest wall and keeps the pleural membranes 'sucked' together. As the chest wall rises or falls, the pleural membranes and lungs must therefore also rise or fall 'in sympathy'.

Q 4. Do you think the pressure in the pleural cavity would become more or less negative during inspiration? Why?

5. Many of the deaths that occurred in the Hillsborough football statium tragedy in 1989, resulted from cracked ribs that punctured the outer pleural membrane letting air into the pleural cavity. What effect would this injury have on the lungs?

■ GASEOUS EXCHANGE

■ Gases in and out

Much of the air pulled into the respiratory passages with each breath is expired without ever reaching the alveoli. This is the air contained in the nasal chamber, pharynx, trachea and bronchial passages, which together make up an anatomical *dead space* of about 150 cm^3. (Measures of lung capacity will be explained later, see page 53).

Gas	Inspired air	Expired air	Alveolar air
Oxygen	20.71	14.6	13.2
Carbon dioxide	0.04	3.8	5.0
Nitrogen	78.00	75.4	75.6
Water vapour (variable)	1.25	6.2	6.2

Table 4.1 The percentage of different gases in inspired air, expired air and alveolar air

The oxygen level in expired air is lower than that of inspired air as much of the oxygen in the inspired air has been on-loaded to haemoglobin in the pulmonary capillaries (page 14). The carbon dioxide level is higher in expired air, as it is off-loaded from the blood (see page 15). The body does not absorb or give off gaseous nitrogen, so the percentages of this only alter due to changes in the percentages of the other gases. Water vapour levels fluctuate with the relative humidity of the atmosphere.

 6. Why is the composition of air in the alveoli different from that of expired air?

■ The exchange surface
In an adult human, the respiratory surface (respiratory bronchioles, alveolar ducts and alveoli) has a total surface area of about 70 square metres. The much divided pulmonary capillaries also cover this area, but only contain 80-100 cm³ of blood at any one time. This small amount of blood spread over such a large exchange surface (visualise it as half a cup of liquid spread over the walls of a small room) means that large volumes of gas can be exchanged in only a fraction of a second.

Fig.4.3 illustrates that there are, in fact, four layers through which the gases must pass:
• a thin layer of alveolar fluid containing surfactant
• a thin layer of pavement epithelial cells
• an interstitial space containing thin elastic tissue
• the endothelial lining cells of the capillary.

The total thickness of this surface is less than 0.4 micrometres (less than the thickness of a red blood cell) so rapid diffusion of oxygen and carbon dioxide can occur.

■ The process of exchange
The data in Table 4.2 indicate the rapid diffusion of oxygen from the alveolar air into deoxygenated blood. In the short time that this blood remains in the pulmonary capillaries (less than a second), it achieves an oxygen level almost equal to the level in the alveolar air. Oxygen is not very soluble in water at body temperature, but this problem is largely overcome by the oxygen being on-loaded to the respiratory pigment haemoglobin. Carbon dioxide diffuses out of the blood until the blood level reaches equilibrium with the alveolar level.

 7. Explain what you think happens to the relative gas pressures of oxygen and carbon dioxide in the blood when it reaches respiring tissues.

■ Efficiency of exchange
Mr Riley's bronchitis prevented him from breathing properly, so insufficient oxygen was reaching his blood across the respiratory surface. The transfer of gases across the lung surfaces can be quantified by measurement of a physiological value called the *transfer factor*. This involves the use of carbon monoxide, which behaves like

Gas	Relative gas pressures (kilopascals)		
	Alveolar air	Pulmonary venous blood (deoxygenated)	Pulmonary arterial blood (oxygenated)
Oxygen	14.0	5.3	13.7
Carbon dioxide	5.3	6.0	5.3
Nitrogen	75.8	75.8	75.8

Table 4.2 Relative gas pressure in alveolar air and blood

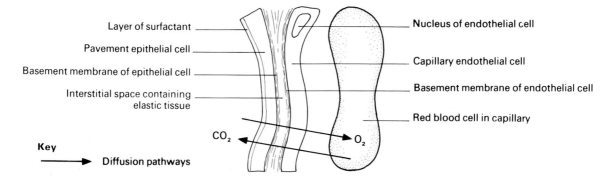

Key

→ Diffusion pathways

Figure 4.3 A section through the pulmonary respiratory surface

oxygen in the alveoli, being readily absorbed by haemoglobin in red blood cells to form *carboxyhaemoglobin*.

A known (small) amount of *carbon monoxide* is added to the air that a patient is breathing, and the rate at which its concentration falls is measured (by the technique of infra-red absorption spectrophotometry). The normal rate of uptake of carbon monoxide into the blood is $4 \, cm^3 \, min^{-1} \, kPa^{-1}$, but if the lungs are damaged by disease, then this transfer factor will be lower. A very low transfer factor will indicate that the damage is causing low oxygen (*anoxia*) in respiring tissues, a condition that can be fatal.

Q 8. Why is it dangerous to inhale large amounts of carbon monoxide?

9(a). The partial pressure of oxygen in the atmosphere decreases with altitude. If a person goes to live at a higher altitude what effect would there be on the transport of oxygen into the blood across the alveoli?

(b). Explain the effect this would have on the person's red blood cell count.

■ BREATHING MOVEMENTS

During breathing movements (Fig.4.4), the volume of the thoracic cavity is altered by muscle action, involving the *intercostal muscles* between the ribs, and the diaphragm, which is a sheet of striated muscle. These structures can be seen in Fig.4.1(b).

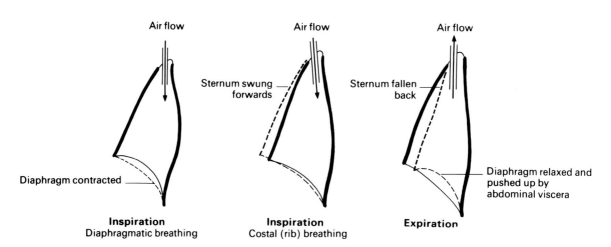

Figure 4.4 The mechanics of inspiration and expiration

■ Inspiration

As you can see in Fig.4.4, when relaxed the diaphragm is dome shaped, arching into the thorax, but as it contracts it flattens, so increasing thoracic volume. At the same time, the external intercostal muscles contract and pull the rib cage upwards and outwards, which also increases the volume of the thorax. Negative pressure in the pleural cavity means that the lungs must increase in volume to the same extent. Air pressure in the alveoli is therefore decreased and air rushes in via the nasal passages and bronchial tree to equilibrate the pressures.

In a forced inspiration the alveolar pressure can go as low as −105 kPa. This means that there is a large reserve of ventilatory ability that can be called on in times of stress or severe exercise.

■ Expiration

During expiration, the diaphragm muscle relaxes allowing the diaphragm to arch up into the thorax and the external intercostal muscles relax allowing the rib cage to fall downwards and inwards. This process is enhanced by the contraction of the internal intercostal muscles, but these muscles are more important in four-legged horizontal animals than in humans where gravity helps the fall of the rib cage. The result is that thoracic volume, and hence lung volume, is decreased. The air pressure in the alveoli increases to about +14 kPa above atmospheric pressure (and up to +133 kPa in forced expiration), so air is forced out of the alveoli, via the bronchial tree and nasal cavities, to the exterior.

■ Ventilation rates and volumes

The volumes of air inhaled and exhaled can be recorded using a spirometer, and Fig.4.5 illustrates how spirometry is being used in hospital for assessing how efficiently a patient is ventilating. The volume of air inhaled or exhaled in a single quiet breath is known as the *tidal volume*, and in an adult this is about 500 cm^3. The frequency of breathing can also be measured, and an average adult at rest breathes about 12 times per minute.

 10. What volume of air would an adult at rest breath in or out per minute?

11. Of the tidal volume, only about 350 cm^3 reaches the alveoli. What happens to the remaining air, about 150 cm^3?

Recording a patient's breathing on a hospital spirometer.

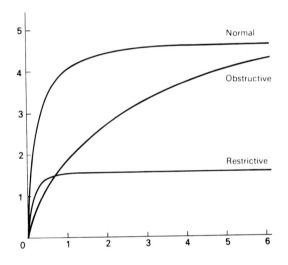

Figure 4.5 A spirometer tracing. In this test the patient breathes suddenly and forcibly into the apparatus to measure the peak flow rate of air out of the lungs. Decreased lung function is found in the obstructive condition where the lung passages may be blocked by infections, and in the restrictive condition where the elastic tissue of the lung may be degenerating

The *inspiratory reserve volume* is the volume of air that can be inhaled by a forced inspiration. On a spirometer tracing, it is measured from the top of a tidal breath. In an adult the average inspiratory reserve volume is about 3100 cm^3 (3.1 dm^3).

The *expiratory reserve volume* is the volume exhaled in a forced expiration, and is measured from the bottom of a tidal breath on the spirometer tracing. In an adult it averages about 1200 cm³. A reduced expiratory reserve volume would have been one of the first symptoms shown by Mr Riley when developing emphysema.

Even after a forced expiration, the alveoli and tubules still contain a considerable volume of air as the lungs are held inflated by the lower intrapleural pressure. This volume is the *residual volume* and is about 1200 cm³ in an adult. The gas composition of the residual volume changes as it mixes with inspired air, and then as the alveoli empty forcibly by elastic recoil due to the high content of elastic tissue in their walls. This creates turbulence which helps the mixing of the air.

Lung capacity can be expressed in a number of different ways:
• *Inspiratory capacity* = tidal volume + inspiratory reserve volume (about 3600 cm³). This is the total amount of air that can be breathed in after a tidal expiration.
• *Functional residual capacity* = residual volume + expiratory reserve volume (about 2400 cm³). This is the amount of air that normally remains in the lungs after a tidal expiration.
• *Vital capacity* = inspiratory reserve volume + tidal volume + expiratory reserve volume (about 4800 cm³). This is the total amount of air that can be exchanged by breathing.
• *Total lung capacity* = vital capacity + residual volume (about 6000 cm³). This is the total volume of the lungs.

Q 12. The disease that Mr Riley died from was emphysema. In emphysema, some of the elastic tissue of the lung breaks down, so some areas of the lung do not expand or recoil during ventilation movements. What effect would this have on: (a) the vital capacity, (b) the residual volume?

■ Stethography
Spirometers are expensive pieces of equipment, and spirometry should only be carried out by suitably trained operators since there are health risks if it is used wrongly. If the actual gas volumes are not required, then *stethography* can be used instead, giving a simple record of the ventilation rate and breathing movements (Fig.4.6).

Recordings can be made after doing measured amounts of exercise, e.g. stepping on to and off of

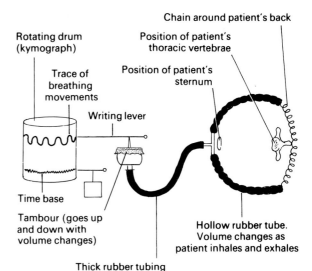

Figure 4.6 Recording breathing movements using a stethograph

a block, either for a set time interval such as a minute, or for a certain number of times. The stethograph is left in place while the exercise is carried out, and quickly coupled to the revolving drum when it is finished.

■ REGULATION OF VENTILATION

Breathing is controlled by a *respiratory centre*, which is located in the medulla and lower pons of the brain (see page 86).

■ Rhythm control
In the resting state the normal rhythm of respiration is that of: inspiration for about two seconds, followed by expiration for about three seconds. This basic rhythm is imposed by impulses generated in the inspiratory centre. This is inactive during expiration, but after about three seconds it suddenly generates impulses which result in the diaphragm and external intercostal muscles contracting and causing inspiration. These impulses are maintained for about two seconds, during which time inhibitory impulses are also sent to the expiratory centre to switch it off. The inspiratory centre then becomes inactive again, and the expiratory centre fires impulses for about three seconds, which inhibit the inspiratory centre and stimulate the internal intercostal muscles and abdominal muscles to contract causing expiration.

The centres in the pons of the brain act antagonistically to control the inspiratory centre of the medulla. The *apneustic centre* sends impulses to the inspiratory centre to activate it and prolong its action when needed, while the *pneumotaxic centre* transmits impulses to turn it off when the lungs become overstretched or full of air.

■ Modification by stretch receptors

Although the basic rhythm of breathing is 'preset' by the above controlling methods, it can be modified to meet the body's changing needs. There are numerous *stretch receptors* in the walls of the bronchial tubes. At the end of inflation, the tubes are stretched, so the stretch receptors are triggered to send impulses along the *vagus nerve* to the inspiratory centre and the apneustic centre. These inhibit the apneustic centre and the inspiratory centre. As the expiratory centre takes over and the lungs deflate, the stretch receptors are no longer stimulated and the inspiratory centre can become active again, stimulated by the apneustic centre. This is called the *inflation reflex* (or *Hering-Breuer reflex*).

■ Modification by chemoreceptors

Chemical stimuli also influence ventilatory activity. Hydrogen ion concentration (pH) of the blood has an effect, but the hydrogen ion concentration is really a reflection of the carbon dioxide level (pCO_2) of the blood. Carbon dioxide in the blood combines with water to form carbonic acid, which immediately dissociates to form H^+ and HCO_3^- ions. Thus any increase in carbon dioxide (e.g. in respiring tissues) will cause an increase in H^+ ions, and any decrease (e.g. in alveoli) will cause a reduction in H^+ ions. The ratio of carbon dioxide tension to H^+ concentration of the blood is sensed in the medulla of the brain, in the carotid bodies, and in the aortic bodies. The carotid and aortic bodies are also sensitive to excessive falls in oxygen tension, and help in the control of blood pressure.

As can be seen in Fig.4.7, the aortic and carotid bodies are linked to the respiratory centre by nerves. A slight increase in the pCO_2 of blood is sensed by chemoreceptors which discharge impulses that decrease the time that the inspiratory centre is active. The inbuilt rhythm of the respiratory centre means that the length of time the expiratory centre is active will also decrease, so the overall *ventilation rate* will increase. Gaseous exchange

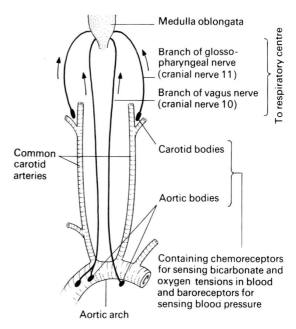

Figure 4.7 The chemoreceptor system for controlling ventilation

can therefore be speeded up and the pCO_2 of the blood falls until the chemoreceptor mechanism is switched off (i.e. *negative feedback*). If the pCO_2 increases a lot, the *depth of ventilation* is also increased.

If the oxygen tension of blood falls below about 70% of normal, the cells of the inspiratory area become starved of oxygen (*anoxia*) and will no longer respond to impulses from the carotid and aortic bodies. Ventilatory movements will therefore slow down and may cease altogether, resulting in death.

13. The normal amount of carbon dioxide in the air is about 0.04%. If a number of people are trapped in a confined space, such as in a lift that has jammed between floors, then the CO_2 tension will start to rise. What effects do you think the following CO_2 tensions would have on those people: (a) 1%, (b) 3%, (c) 6%?

14. During strenuous muscular activity high levels of lactate are produced by anaerobically respiring muscles.
(a) What effect will this have on the blood pH and ventilation rate?
(b) What advantage, if any, does this give the person?

■ THE PHYSIOLOGY OF OXYGEN DEBT

In the Mexico City Olympic games, top class athletes collapsed during races because of the 'thin air' at high altitudes. Their muscles were working at a rate demanding more oxygen than they could get. Thus they got into an *oxygen debt* which can only be repaid by rapid breathing, rest or collapse!

That is the simple story. The full explanation is more complex and needs a background of biochemistry beyond the scope of this book. The full explanation is given in the box below - but be warned - you should look at *Biology Advanced Studies - Biochemistry* before reading it.

EXPLANATION

Muscles require ATP as an energy source for contraction. This ATP is generated mainly by respiratory processes that require *oxygen* to reoxidise the respiratory coenzymes (such as NAD, FAD and cytochromes). If these coenzymes are not reoxidised, then they become in short supply, and respiration is limited.

When the muscle is at rest or only doing a moderate amount of work, sufficient oxygen can enter the muscle fibres to maintain the chemical reactions of respiration. If the muscle is working very hard, the respiratory reactions must generate ATP so quickly that not enough oxygen can enter to reoxidise all the $NADH/H^+$ produced back to NAD^+ for reuse. ATP production can only continue if some of this $NADH/H^+$ is reoxidised, so an alternative mechanism is required. Instead of passing into Krebs cycle, the pyruvate from glycolysis is reduced to lactate using the lactic dehydrogenase enzyme (Fig.4.8). This reaction oxidises $NADH/H^+$ to NAD^+, so glycolysis can continue (although Krebs cycle stops due to lack of pyruvate).

The resulting build up of lactic acid in the muscle is thought to make the muscle feel tired and pain-

ful, eventually forcing rest. At this point, the accumulated lactate contains a proportion of hydrogen from the coenzymes which is equivalent to the amount of oxygen that was lacking. This is termed the *oxygen debt*. When the muscle is at rest, the lactate is oxidised back to pyruvate and the $NADH/H^+$ is regenerated. This requires the person to continue breathing heavily for some minutes after vigorous exercise in order to repay the oxygen debt incurred. Some of the lactate (about 80%) actually diffuses out of the muscle fibre and is reoxidised to pyruvate in other tissues where there is no oxygen debt, e.g. in the liver cells which have a high concentration of lactic dehydrogenase.
(Further details of cell respiration are given in *Biology - Advanced Studies Biochemistry*.)

Q 15. What is different about the histology of a striated muscle fibre that makes it impossible to get enough oxygen into the muscle to allow continual rapid respiration?

16. As an oxygen debt puts muscle tissue at a disadvantage, why do you think the muscle has this structure?

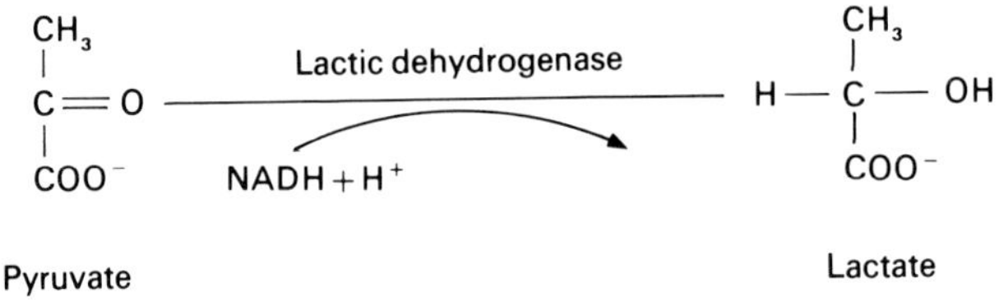

Pyruvate   Lactate

Figure 4.8

CHAPTER 5

WATER BALANCE AND EXCRETION

■ CASE STUDY: ORAL REHYDRATION THERAPY

Andrew was feeling ill. He regretted eating that soft-boiled egg at his Gran's, especially as his GCSE science teacher had told him you could get salmonella food poisoning from undercooked eggs. For several days he had suffered from diarrhoea and vomiting, stomach cramps and headaches, and he was now badly dehydrated, with a low level of essential salts (*electrolytes*) in his blood. He was admitted to hospital, where the medical staff agreed that a salmonella infection was possible, and sent a stool (faecal) sample to the lab for testing. Meanwhile they started him on a course of antibiotics and also gave him *oral rehydration therapy (ORT)* to restore his body fluids to normal concentrations.

The World Health Organisation has formulated a cheap and effective oral rehydration mixture that is used worldwide, particularly to treat those suffering from diseases such as cholera and bacterial dysentery. The mixture contains salts of sodium and potassium, together with glucose to enhance absorption. It is dissolved in clean water and a glassful is drunk after every watery stool or vomit. It seems a very simple remedy, but it is responsible for saving thousands of lives each year. (DIY: One level tablespoon sugar + one level teaspoon salt added to a pint of boiled and cooled water.)

After a few hours of treatment, Andrew was feeling much better as his electrolytes levels returned to normal, although the ORT was continued until his diarrhoea had completely cleared up. The microbiological results from the pathology laboratory showed that he had had a type of salmonella infection, known as paratyphoid. This bacteria has an incubation period of 7 to 24 days, so his Gran's eggs couldn't have been responsible after all.

■ FLUID LOSS AND GAIN

Diarrhoea and vomiting are serious if untreated, because they prevent the normal absorption (in the colon) of water from the dietary intake and from digestive secretions. As in Andrew's case the result may be a severe loss of fluids and salts, and in extreme cases death can occur. An average total of 8.2 dm^3 of fluid is extracted from the blood plasma and released in digestive secretions each day. (This is comprised of: saliva 1.5 dm^3, gastric juice 2.5 dm^3, bile 0.5 dm^3, pancreatic juice 0.7 dm^3 and intestinal juice 3.0 dm^3.)

Q 1. How does this volume of fluid compare with the total blood volume of the body? (See page 34, Question 3.)

2. To counteract dehydration, is it best to drink water, salt and water, or salt and sugar and water?

Under normal conditions, the daily intake of fluid and electrolytes should balance the daily output, a balance that is controlled by homeostatic mechanisms. Over 24 hours, the average urine production by an adult is 1.2 to 1.5 dm^3, the average sweat loss is about 1.5 dm^3, and a small amount of water is lost by evaporation from the lungs in expiration. A normal fluid intake of around 3 dm^3 a day would thus balance the loss. Some fluid intake is from water in foods, but most is regulated by the thirst mechanism and drinking. Sweat loss depends on temperature regulation, but fluid loss via urine is regulated by the kidneys, which are responsible for the *osmoregulation* of body fluids (i.e. the control of the concentration, and hence the osmotic pressure, of body fluids).

Q 3. Stokers who sweat excessively due to heat and hard physical work may develop cramps. How can they avoid this?

■ EXCRETORY PRODUCTS

In addition to osmoregulation, the kidneys also regulate the pH of body fluids and carry out *excretion*, i.e. the removal of toxic waste products of cell metabolism. Surplus amino acids cannot be stored as their amine groups are very toxic. They are therefore *deaminated* in the liver, i.e. the amine groups are split off the amino acids as ammonia. Ammonia would require too much water to dilute it for removal in urine, so it is first changed to highly soluble urea by the *Krebs ornithine cycle*. This cycle converts ammonia to urea using carbon dioxide from respiration, and the carrier amino acid ornithine.

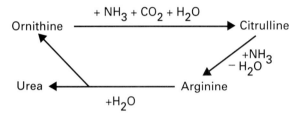

Figure 5.1 Kreb's ornithine cycle

The urea formed in the liver is mainly carried in the bloodstream to the kidneys for excretion, although some urea is lost through sweat. Other nitrogenous excretory products are uric acid and creatinine. Carbon dioxide produced by respiration is mainly lost in gaseous form during ventilation, but some is lost as hydrogencarbonate in urine, sweat and faeces (from bile and pancreatic juice).

■ ANATOMY OF THE URINARY SYSTEM

Study Fig.5.2. Note the kidneys and their blood supply, the ureters, the bladder and the urethra.

Q 4. In what way do you think the anatomy of the male urinary system differs from that of the female?

The walls of the ureters are lined by transitional epithelium (see page 10) coated with mucus to protect it from the acidity and high concentration of the urine produced by the kidneys. The walls contain longitudinal and circular smooth muscle layers to move the urine towards the bladder by *peristalsis* (i.e. waves of muscular contraction that propel contents along a tube).

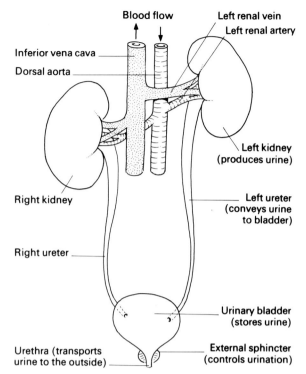

Figure 5.2 The female urinary system

There is no valve at the point where the ureters enter the bladder, but as they pass under the bladder before joining it, the weight of a full bladder presses on the ureters preventing backflow, i.e. acting as a physiological valve.

The bladder is like a deflated balloon when empty, but becomes pear-shaped and extends into the abdominal cavity when full, in which state it stores the urine until urination (*micturition*). It is lined by a 'stretchable' transitional epithelium which is folded when the bladder is empty, and its walls contain three coats of smooth muscle (inner and outer longitudinal, and middle circular). Where the bladder joins the *urethra*, there are two sphincter muscles. The inner one is of smooth muscle, but the outer one is of striated or voluntary muscle, allowing conscious control over micturition to be learned. This is socially important in humans, but also important in many mammals which mark their territory with urine. The micturition reflex is initiated by stretch receptors in the bladder wall which start to transmit impulses when the bladder contains 300 to 400 cm³ of urine.

Study Fig.5.3 and try to imagine the kidney as a three-dimensional structure and then answer the following question.

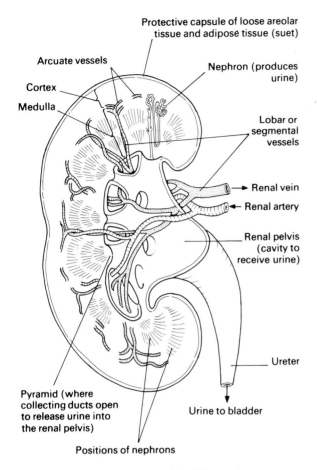

Figure 5.3 (a) Vertical section through the kidney to show the arrangement of nephrons and blood vessels

Labels on Figure 5.3 (a):
- Protective capsule of loose areolar tissue and adipose tissue (suet)
- Arcuate vessels
- Cortex
- Medulla
- Nephron (produces urine)
- Lobar or segmental vessels
- Renal vein
- Renal artery
- Renal pelvis (cavity to receive urine)
- Ureter
- Pyramid (where collecting ducts open to release urine into the renal pelvis)
- Urine to bladder
- Positions of nephrons

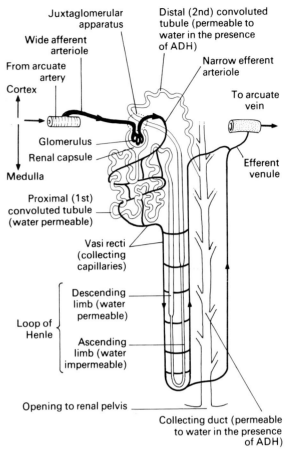

Figure 5.3 (b) A single nephron with its associated blood vessels

Labels on Figure 5.3 (b):
- Juxtaglomerular apparatus
- Wide afferent arteriole
- From arcuate artery
- Cortex
- Medulla
- Distal (2nd) convoluted tubule (permeable to water in the presence of ADH)
- Narrow efferent arteriole
- To arcuate vein
- Glomerulus
- Renal capsule
- Efferent venule
- Proximal (1st) convoluted tubule (water permeable)
- Vasi recti (collecting capillaries)
- Loop of Henle
- Descending limb (water permeable)
- Ascending limb (water impermeable)
- Opening to renal pelvis
- Collecting duct (permeable to water in the presence of ADH)

Trace the pathway through the blood vessels of the kidney that a molecule of plasma protein would follow, from the renal artery to the renal vein. (Remember that protein cannot normally escape into the filtrate and so remains in the blood.)

THE PHYSIOLOGY OF URINE PRODUCTION BY THE NEPHRONS

Ultrafiltration

The first stage in the formation of urine is glomerular filtration, which results in the production of a *glomerular filtrate* in the *renal capsules*. A glomerulus is a coiled knot of capillaries with a huge surface area for filtration. The pavement epithelia of the capillaries and of the inner capsule wall are modified into *podocytes* (foot cells), which are raised off the basement membrane by cytoplasmic projections. The actual filter is therefore the *basement membrane*, rather than the two epithelia. It is only 0.1 micrometres thick and many times more permeable to small molecules (but not to large molecules of protein) than are unmodified capillary membranes.

As illustrated in Fig.5.3(b), the *afferent* ('carrying to') arteriole is wider than the *efferent* ('carrying away from') arteriole so there is increased resistance to blood leaving the glomerulus. As a result, the *blood hydrostatic pressure* in the glomerular capillaries is about 8 kPa (60 mm Hg) compared with only 3.3 kPa (25 mm Hg) in other body capillaries. This tends to force water and small molecules such as sugars, amino acids, nitrogenous wastes and salts, out of the blood and into the capsule, a process known as *ultrafiltration*, or filtration under pressure. The large molecules of plasma protein cannot pass through the membranes and therefore they remain in the blood. The limit of filtration is said to be a molecular mass of 68 000, although molecular shape also has an effect.

However, filtration is not as straightforward as this because the blood hydrostatic pressure is opposed by two forces. The first is the *capsular hydrostatic pressure* which is the resistance offered by the walls of the capsule and by the fluid it already contains. This pressure is about 2.7 kPa (20 mm Hg) and it tends to push some filtrate back into the glomerulus. The second opposing pressure is due to the proteins retained in the blood. These exert a *colloidal osmotic pressure* of about 4 kPa (30 mm Hg) which draws water from the filtrate back into the blood. The *effective filtration pressure* producing glomerular filtrate is given by the following equation:

$$\text{Effective filtration pressure} = \text{blood pressure} - \text{capsular pressure} - \text{colloidal pressure}$$

$$= 8 - 2.7 - 4$$
$$= 1.3 \text{ kPa}$$

The effective filtration pressure of 1.3 kPa produces a total flow rate (the sum of both kidneys) of about 125 cm^3 filtrate per minute.

 6. What volume of glomerular filtrate will be produced per day?

7. If the total blood volume is 6 dm^3, how many times a day will the blood be filtered by the kidneys? (Remember that blood cells are not filtered into the glomerulus, and these cells make up about 45% of the volume of blood.)

■ Reabsorption and secretion
If you have worked out the answers to the above questions you will realise that the glomerular filtrate has to be considerably modified by the nephron tubules to produce only about 1.5 dm^3 of urine a day. Some substances will move into or out of the tubular fluid by *passive transport* (e.g. diffusion) but the process that results in the most change is *active transport*. This is because active transport can occur against the concentration gradient by the use of specific carrier molecules and the expenditure of energy. It can also operate

in either direction, as active reabsorption from tubular fluid to blood, and as active secretion from blood to tubular fluid. The extensive capillary network surrounding the nephrons provides a huge surface area for exchange which occurs via the peritubular tissue fluid (also known as *interstitial fluid*).

Substances that are actively reabsorbed by the tubule cells into the interstitial fluid (intercellular fluid) are glucose, amino acids, proteins (only trace amounts escape into the filtrate but all are reabsorbed) and some urea and uric acid. Proportions of the following ions are also actively reabsorbed according to the body's needs; Na$^+$, K$^+$, Mg^{2+}, Ca^{2+}, Cl$^-$, HCO$_3^-$. Once these substances are in the interstitial fluid, they pass into the blood of the surrounding capillaries by *diffusion*. The active reabsorption mechanisms for glucose and amino acids are particularly strong, so these are normally completely reabsorbed into the blood by the time the tubular fluid reaches the end of the *proximal convoluted tubule*. This is important as they are useful substances to the body. Phosphates, sulphates and nitrates are not reabsorbed.

Active secretion occurs mainly into the distal convoluted tubule, and substances that may be secreted include H$^+$, K$^+$, HCO$_3^-$, ammonia, creatinine, and drugs such as penicillin.

The reabsorption of water by osmosis is particularly related to reabsorption of salts, and depends on differential water permeability in the parts of a nephron, and on a counter current mechanism involving the *loop of Henle*.

■ Water permeability
When solutes are absorbed by the tubule epithelium, osmotic forces cause water absorption at the same time, providing the cell membranes are actually permeable to water. The proximal convoluted tubule and descending limb of the loop of Henle are always permeable, while the ascending limb is always impermeable to water, but permeable to chloride ions, which it actively transports into the interstitial fluid (followed by sodium ions). The *distal convoluted tubule* and *collecting duct* are impermeable to water if antidiuretic hormone (ADH) is absent, but permeable in its presence, the degree of water permeability being directly proportional to ADH concentration.

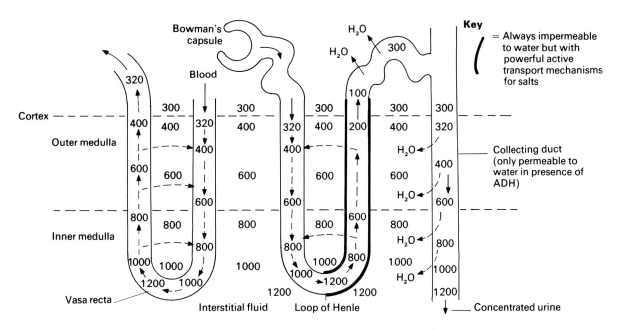

Figure 5.4 Counter current principle. (The numbers refer to NaCl concentration in milliosmoles (dm^{-3}.)

■ **The counter current multiplier mechanism**

As sodium and chloride ions make up 90% of the extracellular electrolytes, you should concentrate on these in the following account of the counter current principle, though similar mechanisms apply to the other ions present. When chloride ions are pumped across the membrane, sodium ions follow because every negative ion must have a positive ion to balance it.

Through the next section refer to Fig.5.4 which illustrates the counter current mechanism for sodium and chloride ions. (Concentrations are in milliosmoles per dm^3, i.e. mOsm dm^{-3}, but in the text they will be referred to as 'units'.)

Observe that the tubular fluid in the lowest part of the loop of Henle, deep in the medulla of the kidney, contains the highest concentration of sodium chloride (NaCl), at 1200 units. As this fluid rises up the ascending limb, NaCl passes out into the interstitial fluid, thus increasing the concentration outside, while reducing the concentration inside the tubule. (Remember that water cannot leave the ascending limb.) By the time the tubular fluid reaches the distal convoluted tubule, its concentration is down to about 100 units.

Meanwhile the blood entering the glomerulus has a variable NaCl concentration, depending on dietary intake, sweating, and other factors (the average concentration is 320 units) and as NaCl crosses the glomerular membrane freely, the same concentration is found in the tubular fluid of the proximal tubule. As this fluid passes down into the medulla, it is surrounded by interstitial fluid with an increasing NaCl concentration. NaCl will therefore diffuse into the tubule, increasing the concentration of the tubule fluid, up to 1200 units, in the base of the loop of Henle. The salt is thus circulating between the ascending and descending limbs of the loop of Henle and the interstitial fluid in the medulla. This maintains a high concentration of salt in the medulla around the collecting ducts.

■ **Regulation of the salt content of blood**

The blood that *enters* the vasa recta in the renal cortex will have a *variable* NaCl concentration in its plasma. As you can see in Fig.5.4, when the vasa recta descends into the medulla, NaCl diffuses from the interstitial fluid into the blood, increasing the concentration to 1200 units, then as the capillaries ascend back to the cortex, the diffusion gradient is reversed and salt diffuses from the blood back to the interstitial fluid. The result of this exchange is that the blood plasma leaving the vasa recta contains a constant NaCl concentration of 320 mOsmdm^{-3}. In this way the system regulates the salt concentration of the blood.

■ The role of ADH – dilute or concentrated urine?

The counter current mechanism of the loop of Henle maintains a high salt concentration in the medulla around the collecting ducts. The effect of this will depend on the permeability of the collecting tubule walls, which in turn depends on antidiuretic hormone. If ADH is absent, the walls are impermeable to water. No water can be reabsorbed from the fluid in the collecting ducts, so a dilute urine is produced containing as little as 100 mOsm l^{-1} of NaCl. If ADH is present, the distal convoluted tubule and collecting duct become permeable to water. This means that water can be drawn out of the urine by osmosis, as the interstitial fluid in the medulla is *hypertonic* to the urine. (The term 'hypertonic' is used in animal studies only and means a solution which is more concentrated than another.) Urine can thus be concentrated up to a level of 1200 mOsm dm^{-3}.

The presence or absence of ADH is controlled by negative feedback. Receptors in the *hypothalamus* sense an increase in the sodium concentration and osmotic pressure (*osmolality*) of the blood plasma, and transmit nerve impulses down the pituitary stalk to the *posterior pituitary body*. These impulses cause the release of ADH from the posterior pituitary into the blood (*neurosecretion*). ADH attaches on to target receptors on the collecting duct cell membranes, and makes them permeable to water so allowing the reabsorption of water back to the blood. As a result, the blood sodium concentration and osmolality fall, and as the receptors in the hypothalamus are no longer stimulated, ADH release is switched off (*damped*). The urine then becomes more dilute and the blood osmolality will rise until the ADH mechanism is switched on again. These changes in blood volume will also cause changes in blood pressure.

The hypothalamus also contains a *thirst centre*. This consists of receptors that are stimulated when the blood osmolality or sodium concentrations become too high. Nerve impulses are generated which make the person aware of his or her thirst, so that he or she will drink, and the blood volume is raised by absorption of water from the digestive tract.

Q 8. If you are thirsty, you might decide to have a cup of coffee. The caffeine in coffee is a *diuretic*, which acts by inhibiting the release of ADH. (a) What effect will caffeine have on your urine volume and concentration? (b) Will the cup of coffee quench your thirst?

9. *Diabetes insipidus* is a disease in which the posterior pituitary function is impaired, so inadequate amounts of ADH are produced. (a) What effects would this have on the volume and concentration of urine and blood? (b) What is the treatment for *diabetes insipidus*?

■ Control of filtration rate

Refer back to Fig.5.3(b) and locate the *juxtaglomerular apparatus (JGA)* of the nephron that has been drawn (not all nephrons possess a JGA). The juxtaglomerular apparatus acts to regulate the *glomerular filtration rate*. It contains receptor cells that are sensitive to the concentration of chloride ions in the fluid flowing through the distal tubule. If the filtration rate is too low then the tubular fluid will flow more slowly through the nephron. This gives more time for reabsorption, so chloride concentration in the tubule will become lower than usual. When this is sensed by the receptors, other juxtaglomerular cells secrete the enzyme *renin* into the bloodstream of the adjacent afferent and efferent arterioles.

Renin acts on a plasma protein called *renin substrate*, or *angiotensinogen*, catalysing its conversion to angiotensin. The target of angiotensin is the smooth muscle of the efferent arteriole which is made to contract. This increases glomerular blood pressure, and hence increases the filtration rate. The fluid thus flows through the tubule faster and so the chloride concentration in the distal tubule increases until it no longer stimulates the JGA receptors. This is another example of negative feedback control.

Another effect of the renin-angiotensin mechanism is that angiotensin stimulates the adrenal cortex to increase its production of the hormone *aldosterone*. Aldosterone raises blood volume by promoting the reabsorption of sodium ions from the tubular fluid into the blood. The sodium ions, followed by chloride ions, increase the osmolality of blood plasma, so water is drawn in to the blood by osmosis.

■ CONTROL OF BLOOD pH BY THE KIDNEYS

The pH of blood plasma must be maintained in the range pH 7.35 to 7.45. This is achieved in three ways. Firstly, the blood itself contains *buffer systems* that operate to make pH fluctuation less likely (e.g. haemoglobin/reduced haemoglobin buffer, carbonic acid /hydrogencarbonate buffer and phosphate buffer). Secondly, the hydrogencarbonate level in the blood is adjusted by *gaseous exchange* in the *alveoli*. Thirdly, there is *homeostatic control* by the kidneys.

When blood plasma becomes too acidic, excess hydrogen ions are actively secreted from the blood into the distal tubule. This makes urine more acidic, but if the urine pH falls as low as pH 4.5, then the active transport mechanisms for pumping hydrogen ions out of the blood fail. The epithelial cells of the distal tubule prevent this happening by producing large quantities of ammonia by deamination. Ammonia (NH_3) combines with the excess H^+ in the tubule cells to form basic ammonium ions (NH_4^+). These ions are actively secreted into the tubule and thus the urine pH is effectively buffered to about pH 6, so that active secretion of H^+ can continue.

If the blood plasma becomes too alkaline, then hydrogencarbonate ions are actively secreted from the blood into the distal tubule. Hydrogencarbonate ions come from carbon dioxide, the main respiratory waste product, so this is an alternative means of CO_2 excretion.

■ CASE STUDY: KIDNEY FAILURE

Ivor Patel had been unwell for some months. He had lost weight generally, but his ankles and feet were very swollen. He felt thirsty, but whatever he drank seemed to go straight through him, as he was urinating far more than usual. He went to the doctor, who took samples of his blood and urine for testing. The lab discovered that his urine was actually more concentrated than normal, and contained a lot of protein, and traces of blood. Meanwhile his blood was low in protein, but contained too much sodium and urea.

The doctor told Ivor that he was suffering from a condition known as *chronic glomerulonephritis*. (A 'chronic' condition is slow to develop and long-lasting.) His glomerular membranes had started to leak, allowing protein to escape into his urine. The loss of protein had caused his blood osmotic pressure to fall so tissue fluid was not passing back into the capillaries. This is why his feet were swollen. Unfortunately the chronic form of the disease is incurable, so eventually all his glomeruli would become ineffective and his kidneys would fail. Mr Patel was therefore started on a programme of *renal dialysis*.

Dialysis is the use of a differentially permeable membrane to separate large non-diffusible molecules from small diffusible ones. The kidney machine carries out *haemodialysis*, that is the removal of toxic waste metabolites directly from the blood, at the same time as maintaining the correct pH and balance of fluid and electrolytes in the blood. Patients with kidney failure require dialysis every two or three days, for up to eight hours at a time.

The patient is first given an injection of an anticoagulant, *heparin*, to prevent clotting. Blood in the arm is then drawn out of the patient's radial artery and passed over one side of a cellophane dialysing membrane. On the other side of the membrane is an artificial dialysing solution, which is at blood temperature, and contains 'normal' concentrations of blood sugar and electrolytes in purified water. This means that the blood and dialysing solution are in equilibrium for the useful substances, so that only waste products and excess ions pass down the concentration gradient into the dialysing solution.

Q 10. Ivor Patel was given the option of having his dialysis treatment at home rather than in hospital. Suggest two advantages and two disadvantages of home dialysis.

11. As long as Ivor doesn't pick up any secondary infections, he could well live for many years on dialysis, though he will never be cured. What would be his only chance of a full recovery?

12. Dialysis patients, and even more so the hospital personnel that work with them, are at considerable risk of infection with blood-borne diseases such as hepatitis.
(a) How can they be protected from hepatitis?
(b) What other diseases do they stand the risk of being exposed to?

CHAPTER 6

FOOD AND NUTRITION

■ **CASE STUDY: ONE MAN'S MEAT IS ANOTHER MAN'S POISON?**

Sarah had always been a happy baby, but at around seven months old, she developed acute night-time colic. She would go to sleep quite happily at 7p.m., then wake up soon after midnight, and scream in pain for up to four hours. The family doctor could find nothing wrong, but Sarah's parents and grandparents were certain there was a medical explanation, and wondered if her diet might be the problem. Sarah's mum decided to revert to feeding her only breast milk for a few days, and then to gradually re-introduce foods one at a time.

They soon started to identify some 'culprits'. Breakfast cereals and teething biscuits caused the worst reaction, but a little gravy with Sarah's vegetables, or a little cheese sauce were almost as bad. The one common ingredient in all these foods was *gluten*, a protein that occurs in wheat flour and is added in the form of flour or just 'starch' to many foods.

The paediatrician (i.e. a doctor who specialises in children's diseases) diagnosed gluten intolerance, and explained that the problem was caused by the immaturity of Sarah's digestive system, so the gluten was not being properly digested or absorbed. He thought that with a strict gluten-free diet, Sarah should grow out of it by the age of three, and fortunately he was right. If Sarah had continued to eat gluten foods, she might have developed full *coeliac disease*. In this condition, the villi of the small intestine degenerate, and absorption of all food, not just gluten, becomes difficult.

Q 1. Many commercial baby foods carry a 'gluten-free' symbol, as Sarah's problem is in fact quite common (though not always recognised). What other food ingredients can be nutritious, or at least harmless, for most people, but can have a poisonous effect on others?

■ DIET

■ Holozoic nutrition

Humans are *heterotrophic*, meaning that we require a constant supply of ready-made complex organic materials that we call 'food'. Basically food supplies us with the materials that can be chemically oxidised to release energy, i.e. the respiratory substrates and materials for growth, repair and tissue maintenance. Humans acquire this food by *holozoic nutrition*, a process that involves four stages:

• *Ingestion*. Food is taken into the body through the mouth.
• *Digestion*. Food is broken down mechanically by teeth, and/or chemically hydrolysed by enzymes to give absorbable products.
• *Assimilation*. The products are absorbed and then utilised by the body processes.

• *Egestion*. Any indigestible matter not absorbable by the body is eliminated by defaecation through the anus.

■ Balanced diet

The constituents of food responsible for providing us with these supplies of complex organic materials are called *nutrients*, and the variety of foods we eat in order to supply our needs is known as our *diet*. A *balanced diet* is one that contains appropriate proportions of all the necessary nutrients for growth, health and correct physiological functioning. It must contain carbohydrates, fats, proteins, vitamins, mineral salts, fibre and water.

If a diet is unbalanced, then the individual may become malnourished. *Malnutrition* is not a condition solely associated with poverty, or restricted to so-called 'third world' countries. It literally means bad nutrition, and includes deficiency diseases caused by a low *vitamin* and/or *mineral* content in the diet, as well as those due to an insufficient *protein* or *energy* content. The nutritional requirements of any individual will depend on many factors, including gender, age, activity, body size and the climate inhabited. These factors primarily influence the *energy expenditure* of the individual and most malnourishment is due to an imbalance between energy intake and expenditure.

The energy value of the three major nutrient groups in kilojoules per gram is as follows:

Carbohydrates = 15.8 kJ per gram
Proteins   = 17.0 kJ per gram
Fats   = 37.8 kJ per gram

Many food packets now provide information on the energy value of the food as well as a list of ingredients. (This energy value is often expressed in kilocalories, one kcal being the old unit of energy measurement, equivalent to 4.18 kJ. The use of the term in scientific work is now obsolete and kilojoules per gram should be used.)

Q 2. In a healthy individual who is consuming a balanced diet, it is usually found that energy intake slightly exceeds energy expenditure. Why?

■ Overeating
When energy intake greatly exceeds energy usage, the excess is converted to fat, and gradually laid down in the body's fat depots. If the body weight exceeds 15% of the ideal weight the individual is said to be clinically *obese*.

Q 3. On average, people who are not obese live longer than those who are. Why do you think this is?

The degree of overeating associated with becoming obese depends both on heredity and on environment. Some people do seem to have a genetic predisposition to obesity, and will become overweight on the same joule intake as another individual who does not put on weight. On the other hand, a child of obese parents may well also become obese, simply because the family eating habits encourage a higher joule intake than necessary.

Q 4. Obesity is said to be a 'Western disease'. What factors concerning the 'Western' diet and eating habits contribute to obesity?

Overeating of certain types of food may cause problems other than obesity. Excess refined carbohydrate also leads to problems associated with the teeth such as *dental caries*. This is the commonest disease in the UK, and may result in tooth loss and gum disease. Unless careful cleaning is done, the sugars found in most processed foods tend to stick to the teeth, forming hard *plaque*. These sugars are broken down by certain bacteria (*Lactobacillus*) in the mouth to produce lactic acid in the plaque. This dissolves calcium under the plaque, and thus gradually erodes small holes through the enamel and dentine of the teeth. This exposes the nerve endings in the dentine to hot, cold or acidic foods, and this causes the pain of a toothache.

■ Undereating
An energy intake that is *less* than energy expenditure will lead initially to the breakdown of carbohydrate and fat reserves in the body. This is the scientific basis for slimming diets, although it should be noted that very often such diets do not 'work' unless extra exercise is taken. The body tends to maintain the energy balance sheet by decreasing its metabolic energy usage in order to adjust to a lower input.

Extreme undereating will eventually mean that the protein components of the body will be used as respiratory substrates. Muscle wastage will then occur, along with further weight loss. This situation is called *starvation*, and if the daily intake remains below the World Health Organization critical level of 6000 kJ for any length of time, then it will almost certainly result in death.

■ Essential nutrients
An essential nutrient is one that is needed for health, but cannot be synthesised by the body. It must therefore be taken in via the diet. Carbohydrates, fats and proteins, together with some mineral elements, are *macronutrients*, as they are needed in relatively large amounts, while trace elements and vitamins are *micronutrients*, needed in only small amounts. Water is also classed as a nutrient as it is essential for life processes. (For further details of nutrients see *Biology Advanced Studies - Biochemistry*.)

■ Carbohydrates
Carbohydrates originate in the process of *photosynthesis* in green plants, and for most people they are the main dietary source of energy.

Glucose is the primary *respiratory substrate*, and some organs like the brain can obtain energy only from glucose, being unable to metabolise fats.

An old Inuit woman 'jigging' for fish

Q 5. The Eskimo, or Inuit people, consume very little carbohydrate, as little is obtainable from their environment. How do you think they obtain the glucose that they require for normal metabolic functioning?

Our chief dietary source of carbohydrate is probably *starch*. This is the main food reserve in plants, and is stored as starch grains in the cytoplasm. The storage carbohydrate in animal tissues is *glycogen*, found in the liver and in striated muscles.

Other dietary sources of carbohydrates include fruits and honey, which are rich in fructose and glucose; milk contains lactose, and sugar cane and sugar beet provide us with the vast quantities of sucrose consumed in Western countries every year. An average daily diet should include between 300 and 400 grams of carbohydrate, which provides between 5040 and 8400 kJ day^{-1}.

■ Proteins

The role of dietary protein is to replace the continual breakdown of protein that occurs each day. The *amino acids* it provides are used for tissue repair, growth and maintenance. They replace the continual turnover of plasma proteins, enzymes and hormones, all of which have a limited lifespan. Our hair, skin and nails are continually being shed so losing protein from our body. Approximately 3.5% of the total body protein is broken down and resynthesised each day. This means that an average adult in good health requires about 40 grams of protein a day, though this could increase to 60 grams a day if protein had to provide 10% of the daily energy requirement.

Q 6. Most adults in the UK actually consume up to 100 grams of protein per day. Unlike surplus fat and carbohydrate, amino acids cannot be stored in the body, so what happens to all the excess amino acids?

The body needs a variety of amino acids for the synthesis of necessary proteins, and these may not always be eaten in the daily diet. For many of the required amino acids, this poses no problems, as the body can convert one amino acid to another (a process called *transamination*). There are some amino acids that cannot be synthesised however, and these must be consumed in the diet. They are known as *essential amino acids*, and if just one of these is missing, then tissue growth cannot occur, and eventually this may lead to death. The essential amino acids required by different species vary; humans must have in their diet a supply of nine of them: lysine, phenylalanine, tryptophan, threonine, methionine, histidine, leucine, isoleucine and valine.

The quality of protein in foods depends on the presence and relative qualities of these essential amino acids. Many animal proteins contain suitable amounts of all of them, and so are of high nutritive value, whereas plant proteins are often deficient in one or more. Maize lacks tryptophan, for instance, while potatoes contain no methionine. An exception is soya bean protein which is recognised as being almost as nutritious as casein, the main protein in milk.

Some unbalanced or 'fad' diets could result in the exclusion of essential amino acids. Vegetarians must take care to eat a wide variety of plant material to ensure an adequate intake of all essential amino acids. Gluten, the protein in wheat flour, that Sarah (see page 64) was intolerant of, is a good source of many amino acids.

■ Fats

Fat forms the major energy store of the body. This is because, when oxidised in cell respiration, it yields more than twice as much energy per gram as the carbohydrate store (glycogen) and because it can be stored in the absence of water. (Glycogen, however, needs three grams of water for every gram of glycogen stored.) It has been estimated that if our energy depended totally on glycogen storage, the extra water required would approximately double our body weight!

The major constituents of fatty foods are *triglycerides*, which are formed by a combination of glycerol and fatty acids in the ratio of one molecule of glycerol to three molecules of fatty acid. The degree of saturation of the fatty acids determines the physical state of the fat at room temperature. If a high proportion of *unsaturated fatty acids* are present, then the fat is liquid at room temperature and called an oil. A high proportion of *saturated fatty acids* results in a solid fat. In general, animal fats, like suet and lard, contain mostly saturated fatty acids, while plant and fish oils, such as olive oil, sunflower oil and cod liver oil, contain more unsaturated fatty acids. Unsaturated compounds contain double bonds in their structure and have a lower proportion of hydrogen than saturated compounds.

Q 7. Margarines are manufactured principally from polyunsaturated vegetable oils (corn oil, soya oil and sunflower oil, for example) but are unexpectedly solid at room temperature. Why is this?

Most fatty acids can be synthesised in the body but a few cannot. These are known as the *essential fatty acids*. The main ones for humans are linoleic acid and arachidonic acid, both of which are unsaturated fatty acids. If these fatty acids are absent from the diet, new tissue growth becomes impossible because they are required as constituents of cell membranes.

As well as supplying us with energy, many fatty foods also contain the *fat-soluble vitamins*, A, D E and K. Most of us eat more fat than we need however, particularly saturated fat, which may stimulate the liver to produce too much cholesterol. On average, people in the UK eat about 50 grams of saturated fat and 12 grams of unsaturated fat per day, but COMA (Committee on Medical Aspects of Food Policy) recommends a daily intake of 37 grams saturated fat and 17 grams unsaturated fat.

Q 8. The Inuit people may need up to 25 200 kJ per day to maintain life in their harsh environment. This means that they often consume up to 300 grams of fat daily. Why is it not feasible to obtain this energy yield by eating carbohydrate?

■ Vitamins

Vitamins are organic compounds that cannot be synthesised by the body, although some vitamins can be assembled if a precursor called a *provitamin* is present. They are absorbed in the gut from the foodstuffs eaten each day, and are vital to health. If they are missing from the diet symptoms of metabolic malfunction known as *deficiency diseases* result.

Vitamins can be split into two groups depending on whether they are fat-soluble or water-soluble. *Fat-soluble vitamins* are absorbed in the gut with fat that has been consumed in the diet. They can be stored in the body, particularly in the cells of organs such as the liver. *Water-soluble vitamins* tend to dissolve in the body fluids and excesses are excreted in the urine.

In Tables 6.1 and 6.2 you can refer to a summary of the metabolic roles and deficiency symptoms of the main vitamins, together with suggested food

Vitamin	Sources	Metabolic role	Deficiency symptoms
A (retinol)	Carrots (supply the provitamin, carotene), liver, dairy products	Responsible for normal epithelial growth (see page 8), precursor of visual pigment, rhodopsin (see page 89)	Dryness of epithelia (e.g. of skin and cornea), poor dark vision adaptation
D (calciferol)	Fish liver oil, also made in skin by action of sunlight on cholesterol derivative	Absorption and use of calcium (and phosphorus), especially in calcification of bones and teeth	Symptoms associated with calcium deficiency, e.g. rickets in children, osteomalacia in adults, poor blood clotting, etc.
E (tocopherol)	Seeds and nuts	May help to maintain cell membranes	Anaemia due to haemolysis of red blood cells
K (phylloquinone)	Sprouts and cabbage	Precursor of blood clotting factor, prothrombin	Delayed clotting time

Table 6.1 Characteristics of fat-soluble vitamins

Vitamin	Sources	Metabolic rate	Deficiency symptoms
B$_1$ (thiamine)	Cereals, yeast extract	Coenzyme[1] for decarboxylase enzymes[2] in Krebs cycle. Required for synthesis of acetylcholine (see page 83)	Beriberi; muscle weakness, nervous system malfunction
B$_2$ (ribo flavin)	Eggs, milk, fish, yeast extract	Component of flavoprotein prosthetic group[3] in respiratory chain	Mouth, ulceration and dermatitis
B$_3$ (nicotinic acid)	Wholemeal bread, meat, yeast extract	Component of the NAD[4] hydrogen acceptor in respiratory chain	Pellagra; skin lesions and diarrhoea
B$_5$ (panthothenic acid)	Virtually all foods	Forms coenzyme A. Required for transport of pyruvate into Krebs cycle	Muscular disfunction (cramps) and fatique
B$_6$ (pyridoxine)	Vegetables, eggs, fish, yeast	Coenzyme for amino acid metabolism. Required for antibody formation	Dermatitis of skin and eyes, depression, nausea, diarrhoea
B$_{12}$ (cyanocobalamin)	Liver, fish, dairy produce	Needed for DNA replication and for red blood cell production	Pernicious anaemia
C (ascorbic acid)	Citrus fruits, tomatoes, green vegetables	Involved with the metabolism of connective tissue, especially collagen	Scurvy; swollen, bleeding gums and poor wound healing
H (biotin)	Kidney, liver, yeast	Coenzyme for carboxylase enzymes[5]	Muscular pains, fatique and depression
M (folic acid)	Green vegetables, liver	Similar to vitamin B$_{12}$	Anaemia

1. Coenzymes are small organic non-protein molecules that are required for active sites of enzymes to function

2. Decarboxylase enzymes remove carboxylic acid groups (–COOH) from molecules during respiration, resulting in CO_2 production

3. A prosthetic group is a coenzyme that is firmly bound to one particular enzyme.

4. NAD is nicotinamide adenine dinucleotide

5. Carboxylase enzymes add acid groups (COOH), or carbon dioxide, to compounds during synthetic reactions

Table 6.2 Characteristics of water-soluble vitamins

sources. Some of the names may be familiar to you from the labelling of breakfast cereals and other prepared foods!

Some people with colds take 4-5g per day of vitamin C to reduce the severity of the symptoms. It helps breaks down mucus, so easing catarrh.

As yet there is no evidence to support the claim that megadoses of vitamin C lead to a reduction in the incidence of common upper respiratory tract infections (colds). Indeed large doses of vitamin C (i.e. ten times the recommended daily dose) can actually be harmful. If such doses are suddenly reduced, the person may get scurvy because the body has adjusted to the higher level.

■ Mineral salts

As well as organic nutrients, a balanced diet must also include certain inorganic nutrients in the form of *mineral salts*. The major *essential elements* include calcium, phosphorus, magnesium, potassium, sodium, chlorine and sulphur. Others are required in trace quantities only, so are termed trace elements, or *inorganic micronutrients*. These include iron, copper, manganese, zinc, cobalt, iodine and fluorine. Minerals are principally concerned with metabolic processes, although some are structurally important in the skeleton, and others act as buffers, maintaining the physiological pH of body fluids. You should already know about some of these minerals, but the Tables 6.3 and 6.4 are included so that you can see how important these substances are in a variety of physiological processes, and how they contribute to a healthy life.

Excess sodium chloride may be harmful to those suffering from hypertension, as evidence seems to suggest it may make the condition worse. However no evidence has been found to suggest that it will produce symptoms of hypertension in healthy individuals who have an adequate water intake.

Iron is lost in the faeces daily due to the breakdown of haemoglobin to form bile pigments. On average this accounts for 0.6 mg per day and tends to be the only loss of iron by men. Women lose a further 1.3 mg during each menstruation.

Element	Sources	Functions	Deficiency symptoms
Calcium (Ca)	Milk	Component of bones and teeth. Required for blood clotting. Activates the enzyme ATPase for muscle contraction	Poor bone growth and development i.e. rickets (see vitamin D, Table 6.1). Delayed blood clotting, muscle weakness
Phosphorus (P)	Most foods	Component of bones and teeth, and of phospholipids (membrane structure), ATP, DNA and RNA. Buffer in the blood	Rarely deficient
Magnesium (Mg)	Most foods	Cofactor[1] for the enzyme ATPase, constituent of bones and teeth	Rarely deficient
Potassium (K)	Meat, fish, vegetables	Needed for maintenance of electrical potentials across membranes, and hence for nerve impulse transmission. Important electrolyte in cells	Rarely deficient
Sodium (Na)	Table salt, bacon	Maintenance of electrical potentials across membranes, nerve impulse transmission. Important electrolyte in body fluids	Muscle cramps
Chlorine (Cl)	Table salt, bacon	With Na^- and K^+, chlorine maintains ionic and osmotic balance in body fluids and cells	Muscle cramps
Sulphur (S)	Protein foods	Component of various proteins, e.g. keratin and insulin	Rarely deficient

1. A cofactor is any non-protein substance that is needed for the functioning of an enzyme

Table 6.3 The major elements

Element	Source	Functions	Deficiency symptoms
Iron (Fe)	Liver, spinach	Constituent of haemoglobin, myoglobin and cytochromes[1]. Activates catalase	Anaemia
Copper (Cu)	Most foods	Component of cytochrome oxidase, and of the enzyme used to produce melanin	Albinism
Manganese (Mn)	Vegetables	Activates enzymes for fatty acid oxidation and bone formation	Malformed bones
Zinc (Zn)	Most foods	Activates carbonic anhydrase for CO_2 transport in blood (see page 15)	Rarely deficient
Cobalt (Co)	Liver	Constituent of vitamin B_{12}	Pernicious anaemia
Iodine (I)	Seafood, salt	Component of the thyroid hormones, T4 and T3, which maintain the basal metabolic rate and growth	Goitre. Cretinism in children
Fluorine (F)	Milk, some tap water	Strengthens tooth enamel	Dental caries more likely

1. Cytochromes are coenzymes which have an important function of electron transfer during the respiratory processes

Table 6.4 Some trace elements

■ Dietary fibre

Dietary fibre (*roughage*) consists mainly of the cellulose cell walls of vegetables, fruits and seeds. It is an essential part of a balanced diet, although it is not a nutrient as such. This is because we have no *cellulase* enzymes to hydrolyse the cellulose, so it cannot be absorbed into the body. In the gut, the fibre absorbs water and swells. This adds bulk to the food and so aids the movement of that food through the alimentary canal. With a low fibre diet, food remains in the bowel region for much longer because the urge to defaecate is suppressed. The result is *constipation*, as too much water is absorbed from the faeces, leaving it hard, dry and compacted. Constipation has been linked to a variety of bowel disorders, including irritable bowel syndrome, colitis and cancer of the colon. There is also evidence to support the idea that high fibre diets reduce the incidence of heart disease, by absorbing cholesterol in the intestine so preventing it being absorbed into the bloodstream.

Examples of high fibre foods

■ Water

Water is a vital component of the diet, because about 65% of the human body consists of water, and all metabolic reactions occur in an aqueous solution. Water loss cannot be completely prevented, and it is important that the daily intake in food and drink balances that loss (see page 57).

■ THE ALIMENTARY CANAL

The alimentary canal (gastrointestinal tract or gut) connects the mouth to the anus, and is where the processes of *ingestion, digestion, absorption* and *egestion* occur (Fig.6.1). There are also a number of structures and organs associated with the gut, which assist in the mechanical or chemical breakdown of food particles. Although the alimentary canal is differentiated along its length, the gut wall has the same basic histological structure from the oesophagus to the anus (Fig.6.2).

The gut wall has four tissue layers:
• The *mucosa* is the innermost layer, and is therefore in contact with the food as it passes through the lumen of the canal. It is highly folded to increase the surface area for the digestion and absorption of this food. There is a mucous epithelium (see page 10) closest to the lumen, and connective tissue behind it containing blood capillaries and lacteals (see page 75). Stratified squamous epithelium (see page 10) is the lining layer of cells in the buccal cavity and oesophagus, and also in the final part of the rectum, so that the outer cells can be rubbed off by the passage of food or faeces. Elsewhere the gut contents become semi-fluid so there is less risk of friction damage, and a different type of epithelium, i.e. simple columnar epithelium, is found. This epithelium contains *goblet cells* which secrete mucus for *lubrication* and for *protection* against the harmful effects of digestive secretions, and other gland cells which secrete enzymes.

Q 9. Why would it be a disadvantage if the epithelium was stratified throughout the gut?

Separating the connective tissue of the mucosa from the submucosa is a thin layer of smooth muscle. Contractions of this muscle cause the *villi*, and other folds of the mucosa, to wave around in the lumen and so come into contact with more of the gut contents.
• The *submucosa* is a layer of connective tissue that contains arterioles, venules and lymphatics, and has a network of *autonomic nerve fibres* on its outer surface. In the duodenum, it also contains *Brunner's glands*, which secrete alkaline fluid and mucus into the crypts of Lieberkühn.

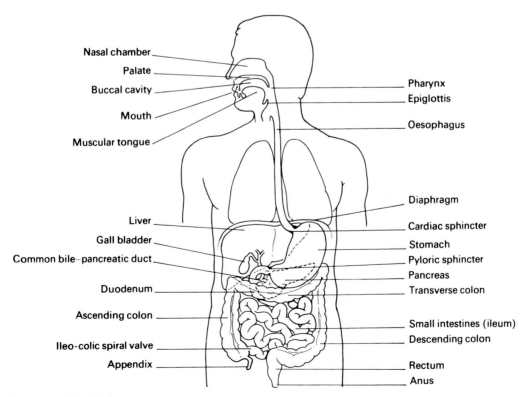

Figure 6.1 The alimentary canal

In the presence of Ca^+ ions, rennin solidifies milk by precipitating the casein proteins out of solution. This slows down the passage of the milk through the gut thus allowing absorption of essential nutrients. Rennin is not present in the gastric juice of adults.

Q 11. Why are gastric enzymes secreted by the peptic cells in an inactive form?

• *Goblet cells* in the gastric pits and on the surface of the mucosa secrete complex chemicals called *mucopolysaccharides*. The most important of these is *mucin*, which dissolves to form mucus, although another important molecule known as 'intrinsic factor' is also secreted. It must combine with vitamin B_{12} before the B_{12} can be absorbed (see page 68). The mucus lines the stomach and offers a good degree of protection against the acid contents and 'protein-splitting' (*proteolytic*) enzymes. Without mucus, the gut could be digested by its own secretions, and the hydrochloric acid could cause ulceration.

Q 12. Stomach ulcers usually only develop if the sufferer is under stress. How could stress cause ulcers?

13. How can ulcers be prevented in people at risk?

14. One type of treatment for stomach ulcers involves the removal of part of the stomach. What changes would this impose on the feeding habits of the individual?

Gastric secretion is under the control of hormonal and nervous mechanisms. The initial secretion of gastric juice is an automatic *reflex response* to the presence of food in the mouth, which triggers impulses via the vagus nerve to the gastric mucosa. The presence of food in the stomach then causes endocrine cells in the mucosa to secrete the hormone *gastrin*. This is carried by the blood to the gastric glands, stimulating them to release more juice. Gastrin is secreted all the time the food remains in the stomach.

The muscular stomach wall churns the food up with these secretions to produce eventually a watery paste (*chyme*). Small amounts of the chyme are passed through the pyloric sphincter into the duodenum for further digestion. The only substances that are absorbed through the stomach wall are glucose (and other simple sugars), water and alcohol, and they do so by passive diffusion.

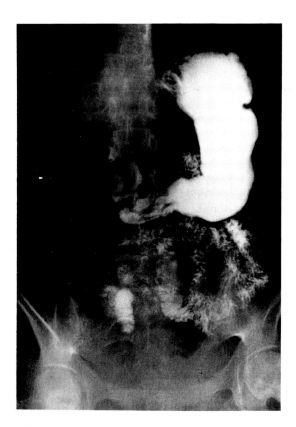

Radiograph of the stomach after a barium meal (ventral view)

■ The duodenum

The name duodenum is derived from 'twelve' as it was once assumed to be the first 12 inches after the stomach. The duodenum receives bile from the liver and pancreatic juice from the pancreas, and the majority of digestion occurs here.

Bile is produced continually by hepatocytes in the liver, and either emptied straight into the duodenum through the *bile duct*, or stored in the *gall bladder* until required. It is an aqueous solution of alkaline bile salts, mainly sodium and potassium hydrogen carbonate, glycocholate and taurocholate, together with bile pigments (*bilirubin*) and cholesterol. The bile salts are responsible for emulsifying fats in the duodenum by *saponification*. The process of saponification is the alkaline hydrolysis of fat to form sodium salts of fatty acids (or soaps) and glycerol. Bilirubin is an excretory product formed from the breakdown of haemoglobin and it turns the bile greenish-yellow in colour (see page 16).

15. What does emulsification mean, and why is it important that fats are emulsified in the gut?

16. What sort of diet would be needed by someone who has had their gall bladder removed?

■ The pancreas

The *pancreas* is a leaf-shaped organ located just under the stomach. It contains both *endocrine* and *exocrine* gland cells (see page 97), with the exocrine portion of the pancreas being responsible for secreting pancreatic juice. The exocrine cells are arranged in groups called *acini*, with a branch of the pancreatic duct at the centre of each acinus (see Fig.1.9). The pancreatic duct joins with the bile duct from the liver, and enters the duodenum.

Pancreatic juice consists of a number of enzymes, together with hydrogen carbonate ions. These neutralise the acidic chyme from the stomach and provide an alkaline optimum pH for the lipases, amylase and proteases in the juice. The l*ipase* digests (by hydrolysis) fats and oils into fatty acids and glycerol. *Amylase* continues where the salivary amylase left off, with the breakdown of starch into maltose. The proteases are secreted as inactive precursors, *trypsinogen* and *chymotrypsinogen*. Trypsinogen is activated to *trypsin* by an enzyme called *enterokinase*, released by the mucosa of the duodenum. Trypsin then activates chymotrypsinogen to *chymotrypsin*. Both trypsin and chymotrypsin are proteases, and hydrolyse proteins into polypeptides.

The arrival of acid chyme in the normally alkaline duodenum cause endocrine cells in the duodenal mucosa to release three hormones into the blood.
• *cholecystokinin-pancreozymin* (CCK-PZ) triggers the release of bile from the gall bladder and the release of pancreatic enzymes
• *secretin* stimulates the pancreas to secrete an alkaline fluid (into which the enzymes pass)
• *enterocrinin* causes the release of intestinal juice (*succus entericus*) by the Brunner's glands and crypts of Lieberkühn of the duodenal wall.

■ The ileum

The ileum is approximately four metres long and its mucosa is highly folded into finger-like structures called *villi* (Fig.6.4). The length of the ileum and the possession of villi both serve to increase the surface area for absorption of digested foodstuffs. The process of digestion is completed in the

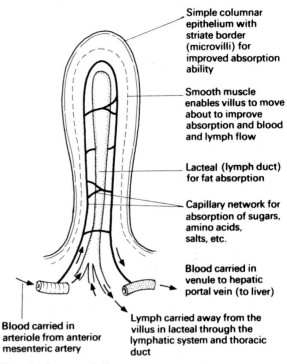

Simple columnar epithelium with striate border (microvilli) for improved absorption ability

Smooth muscle enables villus to move about to improve absorption and blood and lymph flow

Lacteal (lymph duct) for fat absorption

Capillary network for absorption of sugars, amino acids, salts, etc.

Blood carried in venule to hepatic portal vein (to liver)

Blood carried in arteriole from anterior mesenteric artery

Lymph carried away from the villus in lacteal through the lymphatic system and thoracic duct

Figure 6.4 Structure of villus

ileum by a group of enzymes in the succus entericus secreted by the Brunner's glands and crypts of Lieberkühn in the wall of the duodenum. These enzymes include: *maltase*, which hydrolyses maltose to glucose; *sucrase*, which hydrolyses sucrose to glucose and fructose; *lactase*, which hydrolyses lactose to glucose and galactose; *lipase*, which hydrolyses lipids to fatty acids and glycerol; and *peptidases* which hydrolyse polypeptides to animo acids. Intestinal juice also contains hydrogencarbonate ions which maintain a pH of about 9.0 in the ileum.

The contents of the ileum are more watery than in the stomach, and are now termed *chyle*. It takes 3-5 hours for this chyle to be moved slowly through the ileum by weak peristaltic waves, before it passes into the large intestine through the *ileocaecal sphincter*.

■ The large intestine

The large intestine consists of the *appendix*, the *caecum*, the *colon*, and the *rectum*. The appendix and caecum are vestigial (have no function) in humans, although in other mammals they may contain cellulose-splitting bacteria for the breakdown of plant cell walls. The colon is about 2.5 metres long and is the region where much water is absorbed back to the blood. The rectum is a temporary storage area for faeces, and distension of the rectum triggers impulses producing an urge to empty the bowel, i.e. to defaecate. *Faeces* consist of any food constituents that have not been absorbed, cellular material rubbed from the wall of the gut by the passage of food, remaining digestive secretions, and bacterial inhabitants of the gut (*gut flora*). Defaecation is achieved by the relaxing of the *anal sphincter* muscle.

■ ABSORPTION AND ASSIMILATION

■ Carbohydrates
If simple sugars like glucose and fructose are consumed in the diet, no chemical digestion is required; the small molecules can be absorbed through the gastric wall by diffusion.

Other larger carbohydrates must first be hydrolysed to monosaccharides in the ileum. The villus epithelial cells take up glucose and galactose by active transport, while fructose enters by facilitated diffusion. All the sugars then diffuse into the capillaries of the villus, which eventually unite to form the hepatic portal vein to the liver.

The sugar (mainly glucose) that is not required as respiratory substrate is either stored as glycogen in the liver, transported to the muscles for storage as glycogen, or converted to fat for storage in adipose cells.

■ Proteins
Dietary protein is hydrolysed by enzymes into tripeptides, dipeptides and amino acids. The main products absorbed are amino acids, but the peptides can also be taken up. All three products are absorbed by active transport into the villus epithelium, where intracellular proteases hydrolyse any tripeptides and dipeptides, and amino acids diffuse into the capillaries of the villus.

The amino acids are transported to the liver in the hepatic portal vein. Some are used by the liver for plasma protein synthesis, while others are transported round the body for the synthesis of new protoplasm, enzymes, hormones, and other proteins. Excess, or unwanted, amino acids are *deaminated* in the liver to form urea.

■ Lipids
Dietary lipids are digested to fatty acids and glycerol. Short-chained (less than ten carbons)

fatty acids can diffuse directly into the blood capillaries to be transported to the liver in the hepatic portal vein.

Most fatty acids are long chain however. These and glycerol are absorbed into the epithelial cells, where they recombine to form triglycerides in the smooth endoplasmic reticulum of the cell. The triglycerides, along with phospholipids and cholesterol, form fat globules which are coated with protein and secreted into the lacteal of the villus (Fig.6.4). The lipoprotein units, called *chylomicrons*, are carried in the lymphatic system to the thoracic lymphatic duct, which eventually empties into the left subclavian vein in the neck (see Fig.3.11(b)).

Q 17. Which cell organelles will be involved in coating the fat globules with protein and then secreting them?

Some fat is required as a constituent of cell membranes, but most is used for energy production. Any surplus is stored in the body's fat deposits, under the skin, around the kidneys, and in the yellow bone marrow.

■ THE LIVER

The liver is located just below the diaphragm, and is the largest internal organ of the body although the skin covering the body is an even larger organ. The liver receives oxygenated blood via the *hepatic artery*, and also blood rich in absorbed nutrients via the *hepatic portal vein*.

■ The histology of the liver
The liver is made up mainly of cells called *hepatocytes*, (see page 4). These are arranged in radial rows around a central vein, forming functional units called *lobules* (Fig.6.5). The rows of cells are arranged into plates such that each cell is in direct contact on one side with a blood *sinusoid*, containing blood from both the hepatic portal vein and the hepatic artery, and on the other side with a small branch of the bile duct called a *canaliculus*.

Sinusoids differ from normal capillaries in their extreme narrowness, and in that their wall is a fenestrated endothelium. The pores in the endothelium are approximately ten nanometres wide (10^{-9}m), and this together with the large surface area of the hepatocytes means that there is a rapid exchange of substances to and from the blood. Eventually the sinusoids unite to form branches of the hepatic vein which carries blood away from the liver. The sinusoids also contain special cells called *reticulo-endothelial cells*, or *Kupffer cells*. These are fixed phagocytes, and engulf particles of old red blood cells and microorganisms.

Bile produced by the hepatocytes is passed directly into the *bile canaliculi* that run within the plates of hepatic cells, the flow of bile being opposite to blood flow in the sinusoids. The canaliculi converge to form bile ductules and then the bile duct, which carries bile to the gall bladder for storage. If bile salts form crystals, the bile duct somtimes becomes blocked with stones and pain results. Gallstones can be removed together with the gall bladder and although there is good recovery, the digestion of lipids is affected by the absence of bile.

■ Functions of the liver

The liver is metabolically very active, being particularly involved in homeostasis, detoxification, synthesis, and storage.

• *Homeostasis*. The liver is involved in the regulation of *blood glucose*, under the influence of the hormones *insulin* and *glucagon* from the pancreas (see Chapter 7).

The liver monitors the level of *amino acids* in the blood, and any in excess are deaminated to produce the much less toxic urea which is excreted by the kidneys.

Old red blood cells are removed from the blood, and broken down. The part of haemoglobin that contains iron is recycled, while the remainder is excreted in bile.

Liver cells also remove hormones from the blood and destroy them, particularly the steroid hormones *aldosterone* and *testosterone*. This is a very important role, as homeostasis would be impossible if hormones continued to circulate indefinitely.

• *Detoxification*. The detoxification of unwanted amino acids by deamination has already been mentioned. Other toxins in the blood are chemically converted in the liver to less toxic substances. These include bacterial toxins, alcohol, drugs, nicotine and so on. Large amounts of toxins, such as alcohol, may eventually damage the hepatocytes and cause the liver tissue to degenerate. This is ultimately fatal condition is known as **cirrhosis** of the liver.

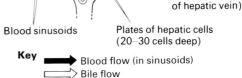

Figure 6.5 A liver lobule

• *Synthesis*. The liver cells synthesise *bile salts*, which are required for the emulsification of lipids (see page 74); *cholesterol*, much of which is excreted in the bile, although some is required for the formation of steroids in the body; *plasma proteins*, including albumins, fibrinogen, prothrombin and globulin transport proteins; and *heparin*, which is an anti-coagulant.

• *Storage*. The liver stores some water-soluble B vitamins, such as nicotinic acid, cyanocobalamin and folic acid, but it particularly stores the fat-soluble vitamins, i.e. A, D, E and K.

Iron from old haemoglobin is stored in the liver cells as a protein complex called *ferritin*. Other minerals that are stored include potassium, and the trace elements, zinc, cobalt and copper.

The liver contains a large volume of blood in its sinusoids and other vessels. It thus acts as a blood reservoir, and along with the spleen, can regulate the amount of blood circulating in the body.

> **cirrhosis** hepatocytes can regenerate by mitosis, but at a much slower rate than the less specialised fibroblasts of the liver connective tissue. Thus when hepatocytes are destroyed (for instance, by poisons such as alcohol), they tend to become replaced by fibrous tissue and the liver becomes increasingly fibrous

CHAPTER 7

CO-ORDINATION AND CONTROL

■ CASE STUDY: EPILEPSY

Jean was about half-way through her A–level courses when she suffered her first epileptic attack. She lost control over her body for a couple of minutes, and she felt like she was whirling round and round in a cage of flashing lights. Her doctor thought that the underlying cause of the attack was the head injury she received last year when she fell off the back of a friend's motorbike, and that the attack had happened now because she was under so much stress doing four A–level subjects.

An epileptic attack involves irregular and abnormal discharges of electricity from millions of neurones in the brain. These result in unco-ordinated impulses being fired off along sensory and motor nerves and through conduction pathways in the central nervous system. Sensory stimulation may cause the sufferer to experience lights, sounds and scents that are not actually present, while motor stimulation may cause striated muscles to contract and relax rapidly resulting in a 'fit'. Certain brain centres may be inhibited, leading to loss of consciousness, or to mental confusion.

An *electro-encephalograph* records the electrical activity of the cerebral cortex of the brain

(see page 86 and Fig.7.6). The electrical 'brain waves' are able to pass through the bone of the skull, and are picked up by a number of sensitive electrodes taped on to the head. Some areas of the cortex are normally more active than others, and the pattern of the brainwaves should be fairly regular and controlled. During an epileptic attack however, all the electrodes record 'spike activity', and the total number of brainwaves per second increases up to threefold.

Jean stayed in hospital for a few days of tests and observation. She had two more attacks, so the doctor put her on a course of drugs that control epilepsy by changing the permeability of neurone membranes. She then went home and returned to school as normal. On medical advice she dropped one of her A–level subjects, reduced her social life somewhat so that she got more sleep, and also took up yoga for relaxation. Over the next six months, as she suffered no more attacks, the drug dosage was gradually reduced to zero. After two years her university doctor signed her off from medical supervision, and gave her a certificate saying she could resume driving lessons.

(a)
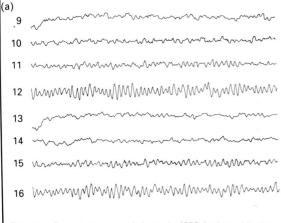

(b)
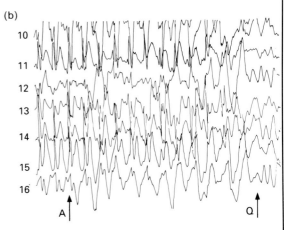

Figure 7.1 Two electro-encephalographs (EEGs) taken while Jean was under observation in hospital: At point A in EEG (b), Jean was asked her address. She made no response

2. What do you think is happening at the point marked Q on EEG(b)?

■ HOMEOSTASIS

It is essential for survival that the physical and chemical processes of the body are controlled. Homeostasis is the maintenance of a stable internal environment by the regulation of these processes of the body within acceptable limits. Human societies can live all over the planet because of homeostasis, which gives a measure of independence from the external environment, while still existing in dynamic equilibrium with it by receiving oxygen, food, water, salts and warmth from the habitat, and returning carbon dioxide and other wastes to that habitat.

Homeostasis within organisms usually involves control by *negative feedback*. This means that if a physiological value varies away from the mean value (*norm*) the *deviation* is sensed by receptors which initiate control mechanisms to return the value to the norm. The receptors are then no longer stimulated and the control mechanisms are either reduced (*damped*), or completely switched off. Control mechanisms may occur via nerve impulses which are rapid or via hormones which (with the exception of adrenaline) are slower and longer-acting.

Positive feedback control is less common but also occurs (for instance, during childbirth, which is described on page 113). In positive feedback the control mechanism acts to push the deviating value further away from the norm.

Many physiological values and processes vary in a regular fashion over a definite period of time. most of these are daily (*circadian*) rhythms, for example temperature control, but some are on different time scales, for example the monthly menstrual cycle.

■ TEMPERATURE REGULATION

Animals vary in their ability to regulate their temperature. The process is best developed in birds and mammals, which are endothermic (homoiothermic). *Endotherms* rely entirely on heat produced internally as a by-product of metabolism, and they regulate their temperatures within narrow limits by balancing heat production and heat loss. All other groups of animals are ectothermic (poikilothermic). *Ectotherms* also produce metabolic heat, but they are less able to retain it and require external heat as well, usually from the sun. They lack precise control mechanisms, and their body temperatures may fluctuate considerably according to the environmental temperature.

Q 3. Cold winter conditions pose particular problems for small animals, both ectothermic and endothermic, because their surface area over which heat may be lost is so large with respect to their volume. How do the following animals overwinter: (a) frogs, (b) butterflies, (c) hedge hogs?

■ The endotherm thermostat

Thermoregulation is only possible if there is some sort of *thermostat* which is activated if the temperature varies from a set point. For both birds and mammals, this thermostat is provided by the *hypothalamus*, which is activated if the temperature varies from a set point. The thermostat contains two centres, one promoting heat loss and one promoting heat gain. These centres receive information from temperature sensors (*thermoreceptors*), which are found in the skin, sensing the surface temperature of the body, and in the hypothalamus itself, sensing the core blood temperature.

■ Warming-up mechanisms

If the skin or blood temperature falls *below* the normal set point, the *heat-promoting centre* of the hypothalamus is activated. This sends impulses along sympathetic nerves, which stimulate responses leading to an increase in temperature. These responses include:
• vasoconstriction of arterioles in the skin, so that less heat is lost from the blood by radiation and conduction
• release of adrenaline and noradrenaline from the adrenal medulla in the brain to stimulate increased cell metabolism, thereby increasing heat production
• increase in striated muscle tone to cause shivering, which also generates heat.

As the *heat-losing centre* of the hypothalamus is inactive, there is little sweat produced and the muscles which are attached to each hair are relaxed so the hair or fur lies flat. These muscles (*erector pili* - sometimes called the *arector pili*) have a greater effect in other mammals. Our hair does not really 'stand on end' but we may feel a prickling in the skin as the muscles contract or relax.

As the body temperature rises back to the set point, the heat-promoting centre is no longer activated. No further impulses are generated, and the adjusting mechanisms will be either damped or switched off. This is another example of negative feedback.

■ Cooling-down mechanisms
If the skin or blood temperature rises *above* the set point, the *heat-losing centre* is activated. This sends impulses mainly along parasympathetic nerves, (see page 85) which stimulate responses that lead to a fall in temperature. These responses include:
• vasodilation of arterioles in the skin, so that more blood flows to the skin and more heat can be lost from it by radiation and conduction
• contraction of the erector pili muscles to raise the hairs, so trapping a layer of insulating air
• increased activity of the sweat glands (actually under sympathetic control), releasing sweat which evaporates by removing latent heat of vaporisation from the skin.

As the heat-promoting centre of the hypothalamus is inactive, shivering does not occur and cell metabolism is decreased.

As the body temperature drops back to the set point, the heat-losing centre is no longer activated, and the adjusting mechanisms will be either damped or switched off by negative feedback.

Q 4. Some pathogenic bacteria and viruses are pyrogenic (*pyros* meaning fire), because they cause our body's hypothalamus thermostat to reset at a higher temperature in response to the infection. Our body temperature rises, and we can become feverish. What possible advantages could this have for a person infected with the disease?

5. What sort of behavioural responses are shown by mammals in response to being: (a) too hot, (b) too cold?

■ Brown fat
Most adipose tissue contains white fat, but in new-born mammals, and in hibernating species, there are also deposits of brown fat. The brown coloration is mainly due to the high concentration of reddish *cytochromes* that it contains, and also the fact that it has a much better blood supply than white fat. (Cytochromes are a group of respiratory coenzymes in which the prothetic group contains iron.)

Brown fat tissue contains many mitochondria, and when stimulated by the sympathetic nervous sytem or adrenaline, it respires rapidly to release its stored energy, primarily as heat. At the end of hibernation, this surge of heat quickly raises the body temperature to the normal set point, increasing the animal's chances of survival. If a hibernating mammal woke with a reduced temperature, it would be sluggish and more vulnerable to attack. Babies cannot shiver to generate heat, so are dependent on brown fat to warm up their bodies when cold. Brown fat is sometimes referred to as the 'biological furnace'.

■ THE PHYSIOLOGY OF NERVOUS TRANSMISSION

(Before studying this section, refer to page 5 and Fig.1.4 which deal with the structure of neurones.)

■ The maintenance of a resting potential
All cells of the body have a resting potential - a difference in electrical charge across their cell membranes - which is essential for the cell to perform its functions properly (Fig.7.2(a)). This resting potential arises in basically the same way in all cells, though it will be described here for a neurone. Nerve cells can only develop and transmit nerve impulses if they possess a resting potential to begin with.

At rest the neurone membrane is impermeable to the *entry* of sodium ions (Na^+) and sodium ions are actively transported out of the neurone by a *sodium pump*. (Remember that active transport requires the use of energy, a carrier substance, in this case to transport sodium ions out of the cell, and it can go against the concentration gradient.) As a result of the action of the sodium pump the resting neurone becomes deficient in positive ions, and has a sodium concentration of about 10 mmoles dm^{-3} inside the neurone, and a sodium concentration of about 142 mmoles dm^{-3} outside the neurone.

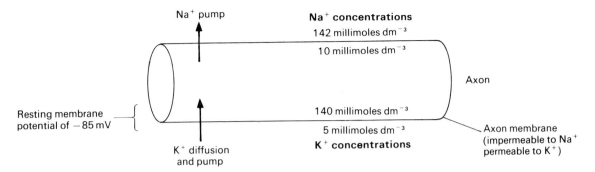

Figure 7.2 (a) Resting potential. Influx of K⁺ cannot quite keep up with outflux of Na⁺. Thus there is a deficit of positive ions inside the axon

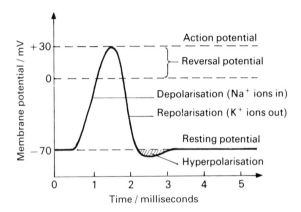

Figure 7.2 (b) Action potential (graphical representation)

At the same time the membrane is permeable to the entry of potassium ions (K^+), and these are attracted into the neurone to balance the absence of positive ions within. This results in potassium ion concentrations of 5 mmoles dm⁻³ outside and 140 mmoles dm⁻³ inside. However, the influx of potassium never quite catches up with the outflow of sodium. This means that there is always, in the resting neurone, a shortage of positive ions *The inside, therefore, remains negative with respect to the outside.* Nerve resting potentials are usually in the range of –60 to –90 millivolts.

■ Generation of the action potential

An *action potential* must be generated before a nerve impulse can be established and transmitted (Fig.7.2(b)). It is generated in response to a stimulus, and it involves a sequence of changes in membrane permeability and in ionic distribution.

The *stimulus* that starts the process may arise from the external environment, such as changing light or pressure, or may stem from the internal environment, such as an altered blood temperature or other impulses. The stimulus causes the neurone membrane to become permeable to the entry of sodium ions for a few ten thousandths of a second. Sodium ions rush in along the concentration gradient, resulting in a reversal of polarity (*depolarisation*). There are now more positive ions inside than outside and the reversal potential is about +35 millivolts.

At this stage, the membrane becomes even more permeable to potassium ions, and these rapidly leave the neurone to balance the negative charge outside. The rather sluggish sodium pump is also removing sodium ions, but at a slower pace. The net result of these movements is that the membrane is *repolarised*, and the polarity is once again close to its resting value. The neurone can then be restimulated to establish another action potential.

This sequence of depolarisation and repolarisation can be repeated many times, so that the impulses flow in *volleys*. A volley of impulses is termed a *signal*. Only when all stimulation has ceased does the sodium pump restore the true resting potential, although the amount of ionic drift occurring during each depolarisation and repolarisation is actually very small to avoid fatigue of the pump mechanism.

The time that must elapse before a second stimulus can set up an action potential is called the *refractory period*. Usually enough potassium outflow must occur to achieve almost the full resting potential. In the large myelinated neurones of the voluntary nervous system, the refractory period is about 0.0004 or 1/2500 of a second. The volley frequency can therefore be as high as 2500 impulses per second. In the non-myelinated neurones of the autonomic nervous system, the refractory period can be as long as 0.02 or 1/50 of a second permitting a volley frequency of only 50 impulses per second.

■ 'All or none' principle

An action potential can only be generated if the stimulus is of sufficient magnitude, a stimulus of the minimum value is the *threshold stimulus*. Stimuli that are greater than the minimum value will not however produce action potentials that are any larger, i.e. it is an 'all or nothing' response.

■ Propagation of the impulse

Once an action potential has been established, it is propagated by *local currents* along the axon. In theory, these can pass either way along the neurone, although synapses between neurones will only conduct in one direction. Each local current at the edge of the area of depolarisation causes depolarisation of the next section of membrane. In this way a *wave of depolarisation* passes along the neurone from the point of stimulation, to be closely followed by wave of repolarisation as the sodium permeability of the membrane returns to its resting state.

In a myelinated neurone, the myelin sheath provides electrical insulation for the neurone, except at the nodes of Ranvier where it narrows. The electrons of the local currents must therefore jump from one *node of Ranvier* to the next. This has two very important consequences. Firstly the ionic drift of sodium and potassium is restricted to the nodes, so the sodium pump has to expend less energy in recovery. Secondly, the jumping of the impulse from node to node (*saltatory conduction*) greatly increases the speed at which the impulse travels. A myelinated neurone of the voluntary nervous system can conduct impulses at a speed of 100 ms^{-1}, while the non-myelinated neurones of the autonomic system only conduct at about 5ms^{-1}.

Q 6. Which type of neurone, myelinated or non-myelinated, do you think the following nerves will contain and why: (a) optic nerve from the retina of the eye, (b) sciatic nerve motor fibres to the leg muscles, (c) mesenteric nerves to the muscles of the gut wall?

■ Synapses

Study Fig.7.3 and refer back to the diagram of the neuromuscular junction (Fig.2.2).

Synapses are junctions between neurones, and transmit signals from one neurone to the next by means of chemicals. They may be *excitatory* or *inhibitory*, and thus have an important homeostatic role in switching processes on and off. *Excitatory* synapses transmit signals from one cell to the next by establishing impulses in the post-synaptic membrane (i.e. the membrane of the cell after the synapse), and can thus enable the activation of control mechanisms in homeostasis. *Inhibitory* synapses will not transmit the signal however, so stimulation of an inhibitory neurone will lead to the

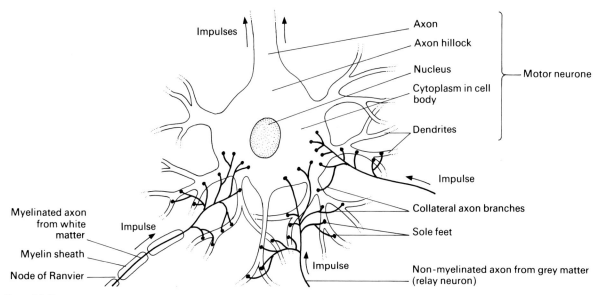

Figure 7.3 Synapses

damping of the mechanism and negative feedback control.

The most common *transmitter substance* in excitatory synapses is *acetylcholine* (ACh), and all such synapses are described as *cholinergic*. These include the neuromuscular junction and most other synapses in the voluntary nervous system, as well as many synapses in the autonomic nervous system.

Excitatory synapses between sympathetic motor neurones and effectors are described as *adrenergic*, because they release *noradrenaline* as their transmitter substance. After depolarisation, noradrenaline is rapidly destroyed by enzymes such as *monoamine oxidase*. Various other excitatory transmitter substances occur in the brain, including *serotonin*, *dopamine* and *glutamic acid*.

Inhibitory synapses release transmitter substances that in effect increase the resting potential so that it is harder to establish a reversal potential. Examples of such transmitters include *glycine* and *gamma-aminobutyric acid*.

Q 7. Depressed people may be given anti-depressant drugs that contain monoamine oxidase. What is the logic of this?

■ Synaptic transmission

Acetylcholine is synthesised in *synaptic vesicles* from choline and acetate, under the influence of the enzyme choline acetylase. ATP from the mitochondria supplies the necessary energy. When an impulse reaches the synaptic knob, the depo-larisation causes some of the vesicles to rupture, releasing ACh into the synaptic cleft or gutter (see Fig.2.2(c)). ACh attaches to specific receptors on the post-synaptic membrane and makes the membrane permeable to sodium ions. These flood into the neurone, reversing the postential and causing depolarisation.

The enzyme *acetylcholine esterase* (present on neurone membranes and on the sarcolemma of muscle cells) then detaches acetylcholine from its receptors and hydrolyses it into acetate and choline (which are reabsorbed into the synaptic knob for recycling). The post-synaptic membrane is then impermeable to sodium ions again and repolarisation occurs, initially by the outflow of potassium ions as in nerve impulse recovery. Once the refractory period is over, the synapse can transmit another impulse, and usually volleys of impulses are set up rather than single ones.

Q 8. Curare is a poison that has been used on arrowheads by South American Indians. It acts by blocking ACh receptors. What effects would this have on the body?

■ THE ORGANISATION OF THE NERVOUS SYSTEM

The nervous system can be divided structurally into two systems, the *central nervous system* (CNS), consisting of the brain and spinal cord (Fig.7.4(a) and (b)), and the *peripheral nervous system*. The

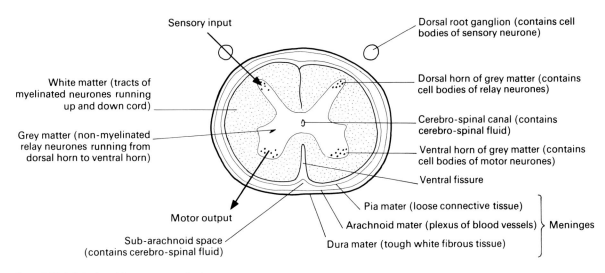

Sensory input

Dorsal root ganglion (contains cell bodies of sensory neurone)

White matter (tracts of myelinated neurones running up and down cord)

Dorsal horn of grey matter (contains cell bodies of relay neurones)

Cerebro-spinal canal (contains cerebro-spinal fluid)

Grey matter (non-myelinated relay neurones running from dorsal horn to ventral horn)

Ventral horn of grey matter (contains cell bodies of motor neurones)

Ventral fissure

Motor output

Pia mater (loose connective tissue)

Arachnoid mater (plexus of blood vessels) ⎫
Dura mater (tough white fibrous tissue) ⎬ Meninges
⎭

Sub-arachnoid space (contains cerebro-spinal fluid)

Figure 7.4 (a) Spinal cord (transverse section).

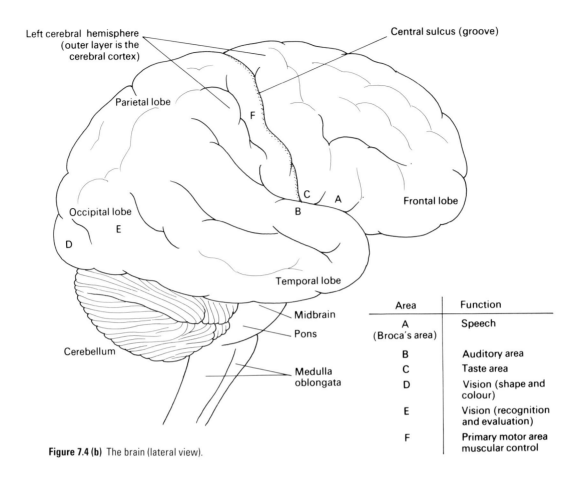

Figure 7.4 (b) The brain (lateral view).

Area	Function
A (Broca's area)	Speech
B	Auditory area
C	Taste area
D	Vision (shape and colour)
E	Vision (recognition and evaluation)
F	Primary motor area muscular control

Effector	Sympathetic stimulation	Parasympathetic stimulation
Iris muscle of eye	Causes pupil dilation	Constricts pupil
Ciliary muscle	No effect	Adjusts for near vision
Sweat glands	Stimulates sweating	No effect
Salivary and gut wall glands	Decreases secretion	Increases secretion
Adrenal medulla	Causes adrenaline release	No effect
Bronchial tree	Causes dilation	Causes constriction
Arterioles to skin	Vasoconstriction	No effect
Arterioles to striated muscle	Vasodilation	No effect
Heart	Increases output	Decreases output

Table 7.1

latter includes *sensory nerves*, which transmit impulses from receptors and sense organs to the CNS, and *motor nerves*, which transmit impulses from the CNS to effector organs, usually muscles or glands. There are also some nerves that are mixed, containing both sensory and motor neurones. Nerves that connect with the CNS in the brain stem are called *cranial nerves*, while nerves connected to the spinal cord are *spinal nerves*.

The nervous system may also be divided functionally into the *voluntary nervous system*, regulating voluntary actions, striated muscles and conscious activities; and the *autonomic nervous system*, regulating involuntary smooth muscle movements and secretions. The autonomic nervous system is subdivided into the sympathetic and parasympathetic systems, which act in tandem to regulate metabolic functions (see Table 7.1).

■ Reflex arcs

The simplest functional unit of the nervous system is the reflex arc. Study Fig.7.5(a) which illustrates a reflex arc of the voluntary nervous system, and Fig.7.5(b) which illustrates a reflex arc in the autonomic nervous system.

 9. What is the main difference between the reflex arcs shown in Fig.7.5?

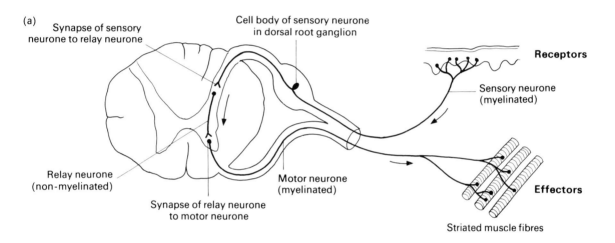

(a)

Synapse of sensory neurone to relay neurone

Cell body of sensory neurone in dorsal root ganglion

Receptors

Sensory neurone (myelinated)

Relay neurone (non-myelinated)

Motor neurone (myelinated)

Effectors

Synapse of relay neurone to motor neurone

Striated muscle fibres

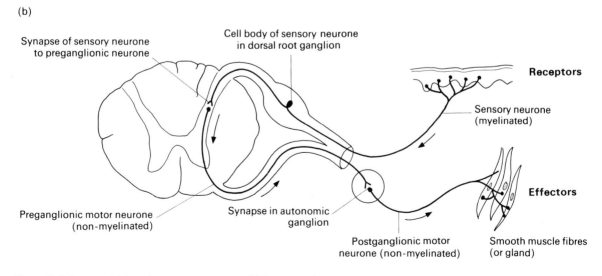

(b)

Synapse of sensory neurone to preganglionic neurone

Cell body of sensory neurone in dorsal root ganglion

Receptors

Sensory neurone (myelinated)

Preganglionic motor neurone (non-myelinated)

Synapse in autonomic ganglion

Effectors

Postganglionic motor neurone (non-myelinated)

Smooth muscle fibres (or gland)

Figure 7.5 Reflex arcs: (a) the voluntary nervous system, (b) the autonomic nervous system

Reflex arcs are effective in three important areas of control.

• They adjust tone in muscles so that the degree of contraction or relaxation is balanced, enabling posture to be maintained.

• They produce protective responses to environmental hazards, examples of such reflex responses being blinking and the withdrawal of one's hand from a hot object.

• They adjust the activity of the internal organs to meet the physioogical needs of the body by homeostasis.

Q 10. The tissue of the central nervous system may be categorised as grey matter or white matter. What types of neurones (myelinated or non-myelinated) do you think occur in each tissue area? What is the functional significance of this?

■ Brain structure

Note that the cavities of the brain shown in Fig.7.6 are called *ventricles*. They are continuous with the *cerebrospinal canal* of the spinal cord, and contain cerebrospinal fluid. This is a form of tissue fluid, its function being to carry nutrients to the cells of the CNS and then carry waste products away.

• Within the *forebrain* is the *cerebrum* (cerebral hemispheres), the *hypothalamus* and the *pineal body*. The cerebrum fills the cranium and has a highly-folded surface giving a greater volume of the outer layer, the *cerebral cortex*. This is 3 mm thick and consists of grey matter, which contains neurones that are concerned with consciousness and memory. Specific areas of the grey matter have specific functions (Fig.7.4(b)).

The hypothalamus is concerned with the autonomic control of cardiac output, blood pressure, body temperature, ventilation, etc. It also regulates the secretions of the posterior pituitary body.

The pineal body is an endocrine gland. It secretes melatonin which regulates gonadotropic (reproductive) hormones and a tropic hormone controlling aldosterone production by the adrenal cortex. The pineal body is of evolutionary interest, as in early chordates, it was a third eye on the top of the head, and can still be seen as such in a few animals, such as lampreys.

• The *midbrain* includes the *corpora quadrigemina* which are relay centres for visual and auditory impulses to the cerebrum.

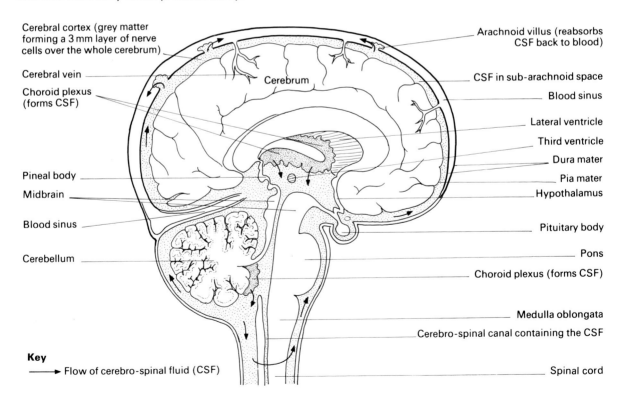

Figure 7.6 The brain (transverse section)

• The *hind brain* contains the *cerebellum* and *medulla oblongata*. The cerebellum also has a folded surface area to accommodate more grey matter. It is concerned with the subconscious movements in striated muscles that result in muscular co-ordination, balance and maintenance of posture. It receives impulses from proprioceptors in muscles and joints, and from the vestibular apparatus of the ear which senses movements of the head relative to gravity. The medulla oblongata contains centres controlling heartbeat, ventilation, vomiting and swallowing, and is the part of the brain from which the twelve pairs of cranial nerves originate. Many of the descending motor nerve tracts (white matter/myelinated fibres) from the cerebellum and cerebrum cross over in the medulla. Thus the right side of the brain controls the left side of the body, and the left side of the brain controls the right side of the body. Normally the various parts of the brain co-ordinate well together. Jean's co-ordination of function was impaired during her epileptic fit (see page 78).

Q 11. A stroke occurs when a blood vessel in the brain becomes either blocked or damaged. The tissue supplied by the vessel may itself be damaged by this and may be destroyed. The part of the brain where the damage occurs determines the precise loss of function to the patient. Where would the damage probably be if the patient: (a) had lost the ability to speak, (b) was suffering severe dizziness, (c) had abnormal heart rhythms, (d) had general paralysis of the left side of the body?

■ RECEPTORS AND SENSE ORGANS

Receptors are cells that are activated by stimuli, which are changes in the internal or external environments. Once activated, they initiate impulses along sensory nerves to the CNS, so that suitable responses may be made.

Q 12. Name three types of receptor cell which monitor the external environment and state where they occur.

Many receptors are grouped together as *sense organs* performing particular functions. These include the eyes, ears, taste buds, and the carotid and aortic bodies.

■ STRUCTURE AND FUNCTION OF THE EYE

The eyes are the sense organs of sight, or vision. They are concerned with the focusing of both near and distant objects, the perception of black and white and of colours, the perception of distance and three dimensions, and visual acuity (the ability to perceive detail).

■ External features of the eye and eyeball
The eyes lie protected in bony sockets (*orbits*) in the skull, to which they are attached by striated external eye muscles (Fig.7.7). A thick transparent mucous membrane, called the *conjunctiva*, covers and protects the front of the eye and also lines the

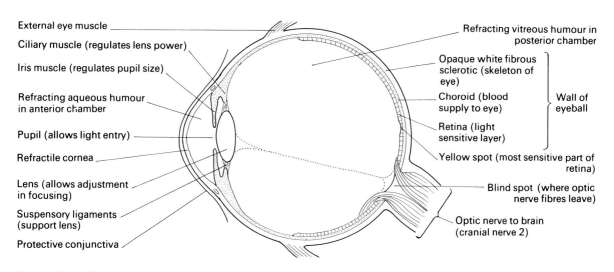

External eye muscle
Ciliary muscle (regulates lens power)
Iris muscle (regulates pupil size)
Refracting aqueous humour in anterior chamber
Pupil (allows light entry)
Refractile cornea
Lens (allows adjustment in focusing)
Suspensory ligaments (support lens)
Protective conjunctiva

Refracting vitreous humour in posterior chamber
Opaque white fibrous sclerotic (skeleton of eye)
Choroid (blood supply to eye) } Wall of eyeball
Retina (light sensitive layer)
Yellow spot (most sensitive part of retina)
Blind spot (where optic nerve fibres leave)
Optic nerve to brain (cranial nerve 2)

Figure 7.7 Eyeball (vertical section)

insides of the eyelids. Lashes on the eyelids help keep foreign material out of the eye and special sebaceous glands secrete a lubricating fluid to prevent the lids sticking. There are also *lacrimal* (tear) *glands* in the upper outer corner of each orbit secreting tears that lubricate and clean the conjunctiva, before draining into the nasal chamber through lacrimal ducts.

The wall of the eye has three layers:
• The outer layer is the tough white fibrous *sclerotic* coat. As well as protecting the eyeball, it has two important roles, in focusing, and in providing a firm surface for muscle attachment. The part of the sclerotic at the front of the eye is called the *cornea*. Here it is transpranent, highly refractile and bulges outwards, and is thus able to bend light rays inwards. Behind this, the sclerotic is opaque and forms the insertion for the striated external muscles that move the eye, and the origin for the smooth internal muscles that adjust pupil aperture and lens curvature.
• The next layer is the *choroid*, which is rich in blood vessels and also pigmented. The pigment absorbs the light after it has passed through the retina, and so reduces internal reflection. At the front of the eye the choroid forms the radial and circular smooth muscles of the *iris*. These muscles regulate the size of the *pupil* to control the amount of light entering the posterior chamber of the eye. Pigmentation of the iris ensures that light can only enter via the pupil. The choroid also forms the *ciliary muscle* which regulates the focusing power of the lens by altering its curvature. It is attached to the lens by suspensory ligaments.
• The inner layer is the *retina* which lies over the choroid up to the margins of the ciliary muscles. It consists of a single layer of pigmented epithelial cells, in front of which are light-sensitive cells (light receptors), called *rods* and *cones*. The retina also contains neurones from these light receptors, that eventually synapse to form the *optic nerve* carrying visual impulses to the brain. The *fovea centralis* (yellow spot) of the retina contains the highest concentration of cones and is the most sensitive part of the retina. It is situated on the optical axis of the lens, at its *focal point*. Where the nerve fibres leave the retina as the optic nerve, there is no room for receptors, so this region is known as the *blind spot*.

■ Within the eyeball

The *lens* is formed of layers of transparent epithelial cells enclosed in an elastic coat. It is biconvex in shape, but since it is elastic, its curvature can be

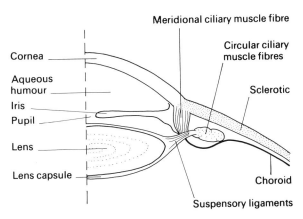

Figure 7.8 (a) Accommodation for near and distant vision. When the meridional fibres contract they pull the suspensory ligaments forward, slackening them. When the circular fibres contract they reduce the circle size, also slackening the suspensory ligaments. This allows the elastic lens to become thicker with more focusing power for near vision. In distant vision the muscles are relaxed, suspensory ligaments are taut and the lens is thin.

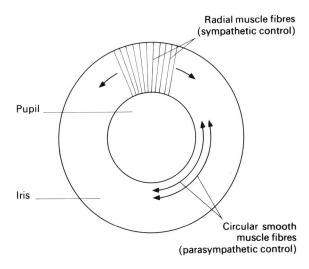

Figure 7.8 (b) The pupil reflex. The iris contains circular and radial smooth muscle fibres. These contract and relax antagonistically to adjust the pupil size

altered as the tension on the suspensory ligaments is adjusted by the ciliary muscles. The curvature required to focus a near object is more than that required to focus a distant one (Fig.7.8).

Q 13. In short sight (*myopia*), either the lens is too curved, or the eyeball is too deep. In long sight (*hypermetropia*), either the lens is too flat, or the eyeball too shallow. What effects will these conditions have on the focusing of the eye and how can they be remedied?

The anterior chamber of the eye is filled with a fluid called *aqueous humour*, and the posterior chamber is filled with a semi-fluid mass called the vitreous humour. The hydrostatic pressure of these fluids maintains the shape of the eyeball, and they also bend light rays towards the fovea and so assist in focusing images.

■ Structure of the retina

 14. Look carefully at Fig.7.9. Why is the retina said to be inverted?

Rods are concerned with black and white vision because they are sensitive to dim light. Several rods synapse to one optic nerve fibre, so this allows the adding together (*summation*) of the signals from several rods to result in a 'better picture'. *Cones* are colour sensitive, but require bright light because they have no summation effect. Only one cone synapses to one optic nerve fibre which it must depolarise. The presence of cones enables the eye to have greater *visual acuity* (ability to distinguish detail) than if only rods were present, as stimulation of adjacent cones by separate light signals will set up impulses in separate optic nerve fibres to the brain. Stimulation of two or more adjacent rods by separate light signals may still only send impulses along one optic nerve fibre. The rods and cones act as *transducers*, converting light energy into electrical energy in the form of nerve impulses. This function depends on the chemistry of the visual pigments that the cells contain.

■ Chemistry of rod vision

Vitamin A is the chemical used by rods and cones for the synthesis of light-sensitive substances. On absorption into the rod or cone, vitamin A is dehydrogenated, using NAD, to form *retinene*. In rods this immediately combines with a protein called *scotopsin* to form the light-sensitive chemical, *rhodopsin* which accumulates in the dark. When exposed to dim light of any wavelength within the visible spectrum (400 - 700 nm), some of the rhodopsin is at once changed into unstable intermediates which rapidly break down to retinene and scotopsin. Rhodopsin is then reformed by enzyme action during a dark period (e.g. blinking). The intermediates bear ionic charges which upset the ionic balance of sodium and potassium across the rod membrane, leading to *depolarisation*. Nerve impulses are thus established, and are relayed to the *visual cortex* of the brain and interpreted as black and white vision.

In bright light rhodopsin is bleached to retinene and scotopsin more quickly than it can be resynthesised, so rods cannot operate. This is the reason why it takes time for your eyes to adjust to the darkness when you first turn a light off at night. The *dark adaptation period* is the time required for rhodopsin to be regenerated by the rod cells. This is not the same as *night blindness* which is a medical condition, resulting from vitamin A

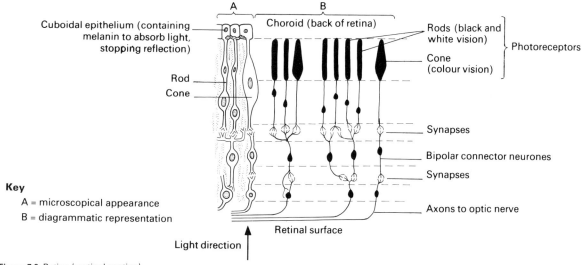

Key
A = microscopical appearance
B = diagrammatic representation

Figure 7.9 Retina (vertical section)

deficiency. Night blindness sufferers cannot see in dim light because they possess insufficient rhodopsin. (If the deficiency is very severe the rhodopsin in cones can also be affected resulting in total blindness).

■ Chemistry of cone vision

There are three types of cone, one responding best to red light, one to green light and the third to blue light. In cones, retinene combines with proteins called *photopsins* to form *cone rhodopsins*. The three types of cone probably contain different combinations of retinene and photopsin, each with a different *light absorption spectrum* and thus are bleached by different wavelengths. The light must be bright enough in order to bleach cone rhodopsins back to retinene and photopsin. Depolarisation occurs as in rods, and the rhodopsin regenerates best during darkness.

If cones of two or three colours are stimulated by light, the signal to the brain will consist of a mosaic of impulses from each type of cell. This can be interpreted in the visual cortex as a colour, or colours, that are intermediate to the red, green, or blue.

■ STRUCTURE AND FUNCTION OF THE EAR

Ears are concerned with *hearing*, or the perception of sound, in terms of pitch, loudness, direction, and colour or timbre, (e.g. trumpet quality or flute quality). The ears also contain gravity sensors, so are important in the maintenance of *balance* and posture.

The outer and middle parts of the ear are concerned with directing sound waves towards the inner ear where the receptors are located. Sound is transmitted through air or water, as vibrations of the air or water. Sound waves are *longitudinal*. This means that the vibrations occur in the same direction as the wave is travelling. These features of sound are used in the ear, where the sound vibrations set up a chain reaction of movement in the tympanic membrane, middle ear ossicles, and inner ear fluids.

■ Ear structure

• The *external ear* is structurally designed to collect sound waves and direct them to the middle ear (Fig.7.10). The external ear consists of the *pinna*, the *external auditory canal* and the *tympanic membrane*.

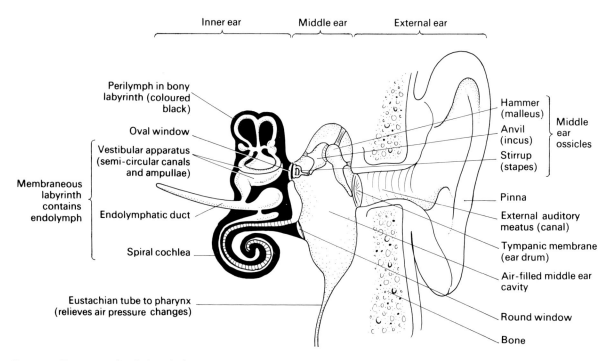

Figure 7.10 Ear structure (vertical section)

The pinna is made of elastic cartilage covered by skin, and it is attached to the skull by muscles and ligaments. In most mammals the pinna can be moved in order to determine the direction from which a sound is coming. This ability is lost in most humans. Sound direction must be determined by the brain analysing the slight differences in sound waves from a single source entering each ear.

The external auditory canal is a tube 2.5 cm in length, leading to the tympanic membrane. There are protective hairs and glands at the entrance of the canal that secrete a waxy substance, probably to repel water from entering the ear.

The ear drum (*tympanic membrane*) is a thin membrane of fibrous connective tissue lined by skin on the outside and mucous membrane on the inside. It separates the outer and middle ears, and sound waves passing along the auditory canal will cause it to vibrate.

• The *middle ear* cavity contains air, and communicates with the inner ear via the round and oval windows. If external air pressure changes, then the air pressure in the cavity can be adjusted by opening the *Eustachian tube* to the back of the throat (e.g. by swallowing or yawning). The middle ear contains a row of three small bones, or auditory *ossicles*; the *hammer* (malleus), attached to the tympanic membrane, the *anvil* (incus), and the *stirrup* (stapes), attached to the oval window (Fig. 7.10). Vibrations of the tympanic membrane are thus transmitted across the middle ear to the oval window.

The ossicles articulate with each other via synovial joints and their position is maintained to the wall of the middle ear chamber by ligaments. The tympanic membrane has an area of about 70 mm^2, whereas the oval window has an area of 3.2 mm^2. This means that 22 times the amount of sound energy can be collected by the tympanic membrane than by the oval window, and the energy of the mechanical vibrations produced in the oval window is 22 times greater than it would be without the tympanic membrane and ossicles. It is now great enough to overcome the inertia of the *perilymph* and *endolymph fluids* and to set up vibrations in them. Thus the middle ear acts as an amplifier.

• The *inner ear* consists of a *bony labyrinth*, or collection of cavities in the temporal bone of the skull. This contains perilymph, which supports and protects the *membraneous labyrinth* floating in it. The membraneous labyrinth mostly contains endolymph and functionally is divided into the *cochlea*, concerned with sound perception, and the *vestibular apparatus* (utriculus, sacculus, three semicircular canals, and three ampullae), concerned with balance reflexes.

■ **Hearing**

Vibrations of the oval window set up waves in the *perilymph* of the vestibular canal (Fig.7.11). The waves create pressure changes which move *Reissner's membrane* and so set up pressure changes in the endolymph of the cochlea duct (median canal). These move the *basilar membrane*, setting up waves in the perilymph of the tympanic duct which are discharged to the

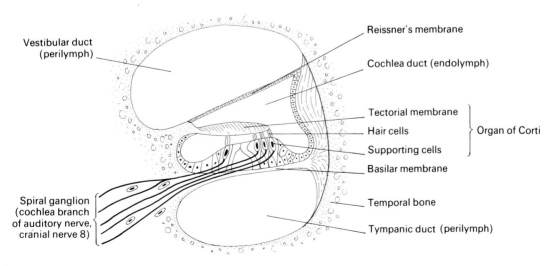

Figure 7.11 Cochlea structure (transverse section)

Vestibular duct (perilymph)

Reissner's membrane

Cochlea duct (endolymph)

Tectorial membrane
Hair cells
Supporting cells
Organ of Corti

Basilar membrane

Spiral ganglion (cochlea branch of auditory nerve, cranial nerve 8)

Temporal bone

Tympanic duct (perilymph)

middle ear by movements of the round window. When the basilar membrane vibrates it pushes the hair cells of the *organ of Corti* against the *tectorial membrane*. The subsequent distortion of the sensory hairs results in depolarisation of the hair cells, and generation of impulses through the cochlea branch of the auditory nerve to the brain.

■ High or low?

The *pitch* of a sound is determined by its *frequency* of vibration; high frequencies giving high notes. The principle of high and low pitch can be illustrated by considering a single string of a violin or guitar. When this string is plucked, the pitch of the note produced will depend on two things: the tightness, or tension, of the string; and the thickness, or mass, of the string. Increased tension will permit higher levels of vibration and so higher notes, and vice versa. A greater mass to be moved by the vibration will cause more inertia, so a lower rate of vibration and low notes, and vice versa.

Exactly the same principle applies in the cochlea. The tension of the basilar membrane varies along its length, being greatest at the base of the cochlea. Only a short distance of basilar membrane is vibrating at this point, so the mass of perilymph and endolymph to be moved is small. The combination of high tension and low mass means that the hair cells at the base of the cochlea are sensitive to high-pitched notes. Low notes are sensed towards the tip of the cochlea however, where the tension of the basilar membrane is less and as a longer length of cochlea is involved, a greater mass of perilymph and endolymph must be moved.

■ Loud or soft

The loudness of the sound is determined by the *amplitude* of the sound waves in the air, which are transduced (converted) to similar-sized waves in the perilymph and endolymph. *Small waves* for instance, cause very little distortion of the hair cells. This means that only about one impulse per second will be fired off to the brain, and this is heard as *quiet* sound.

Larger waves cause much greater distortion of the hair cells. Up to 1000 impulses per second may be generated, and the brain registers this as *loud* noise. Long exposure to loud noise can result in deafness as the hair cells become permanently distorted and start to degenerate.

Audiometry involves the measurement of hearing *loss*, in which the patient is presented with

Recording an audiogram. The patient sits in a soundproof room behind the glass screen and is presented with pure tones at various decibel (dB) levels and pitches (frequencies). The patient responds if they hear the tone. Each ear is tested separately

pure tones at different pitches and intensities, and then asked to indicate whether the sound is heard or not.

Q 15. The audiograms A and B in Fig.7.12(a) were taken from two teenagers, known to their friends as Library Lil and Disco Dan. (a) Comment on the results you see, and suggest what could have caused the difference between them? (b) Can Lil and Dan both hear speech, and if not, what remedy is there?

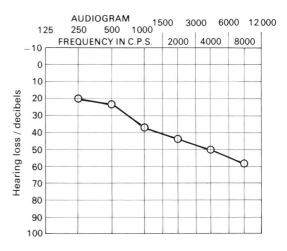

Figure 7.12 (a) Audiogram of left ear (Lil)

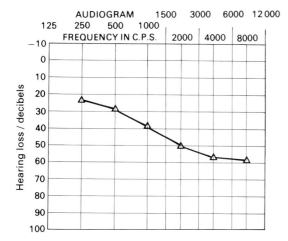

Figure 7.12 (b) Audiogram of right ear (Lil)

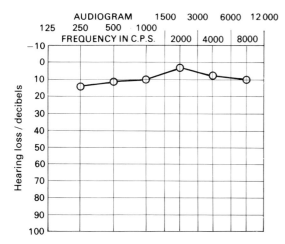

Figure 7.12 (c) Audiogram of left ear (Dan)

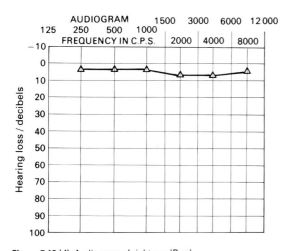

Figure 7.12 (d) Audiogram of right ear (Dan)

■ Balance and equilibrium

There are two types of equilibrium involved in balance. The orientation of the body and the position of the head relative to the ground (gravity) requires a *static equilibrium*, while the movement of the head in relation to sudden body movements, such as rotation, acceleration or deceleration, requires a *dynamic equilibrium*.

• The *maculae* (Fig.7.13(a) and (b)) are located within the *utricle* and *saccule* of the vestibular apparatus. They provide sensory information to the brain concerning the orientation of the head in space. So, these are the receptors concerned with static equilibrium. The maculae contain *otoliths*, which are crystals of calcium carbonate, that are much denser than the surrounding endolymph. They will therefore have considerable inertia, meaning that as the head moves, the otoliths drag behind and distort the gelatinous layer. This pulls on the sensory hairs of the cells, causing depolaristion. Nerve impulses are fired off along the vestibular branch of the auditory nerve to the brain, which then despatches impulses along motor neurones to leg and body muscles, adjusting their tone to maintain balance.

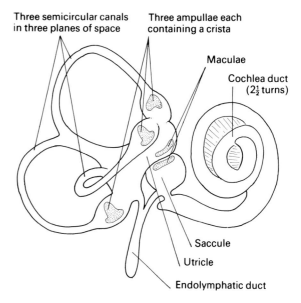

Figure 7.13 (a) The vestibular apparatus. Membraneous labyrinth (contains endolymph)

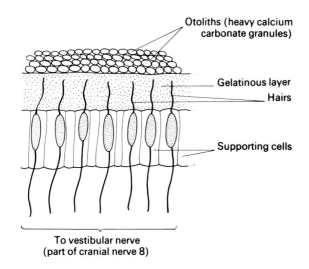

Figure 7.13 (b) Macula (vertical section). The otoliths move with gravity as the head moves, distorting the gelatinous layer. This depolarises the hair cells setting up nerve impulses

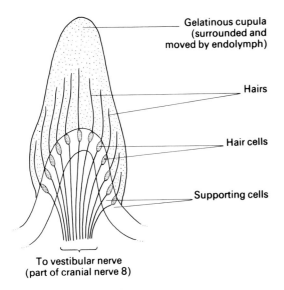

Figure 7.13 (c) Christa (vertical section). The gelatinous cupula moves with gravity as the head moves, thus distorting the sensory hairs

• The *ampullae* are the swollen ends of the three *semicircular canals*. They contain *cristae* (Fig.7.13(c)) which are the receptors that help to maintain dynamic equilibrium. As you can see from Fig. 37.13(a) the semicircular canals are arranged in three different planes, so any movement of the head will produce a flow of endolymph in at least one canal. As the endolymph flows, it will displace the gelatinous layer (*cupula*) to one side, thus stretching the sensory hairs. This depolarises the hair cells and generates impulses along the vestibular nerve to the brain. Impulses are then sent to the appropriate muscles to compensate for the movement, and so balance the body.

Q 16. If you spin round vigorously for a few moments and then stop suddenly, why do you feel dizzy and why do your eyes roll?

17. What part of the brain is mainly concerned with posture and balance?

■ THE ENDOCRINE SYSTEM

Although movement, sensitivity, and many metabolic functions are monitored and controlled by nerve impulses, most long-term growth and metabolism is regulated by hormones. With the exception of adrenaline, hormones act *slowly* and in a more sustained way than nerve impulses, the effects of which are transitory.

A hormone is a biochemical messenger secreted by an endocrine gland into the blood (in animals), and then carried by the blood to a specific target organ, or cell, where it exerts a particular effect. Examples of endocrine glands include the *pituitary*, *thyroid*, *adrenal bodies* and *islets of Langerhans*. The pituitary is sometimes referred to as the 'master' gland since its secretions control the other glands, although the pituitary is in turn controlled by the hypothalamus. As well as specialist endocrine glands, a number of other organs produce hormones. The stomach for instance, secretes *gastrin* which controls the flow of gastric juice; the duodenum produces *secretin* which regulates the flow of pancreatic juice; the testes produce *testosterone* (male sex hormone); and the ovaries secrete *oestrogen* and *progesterone* (female sex hormones).

■ The pituitary body (hypophysis)
The pituitary body (Fig.7.14) consists of two portions that have developed from different embryonic tissues.
• The posterior lobe (*neurohypophysis*) is formed in the embryo from a downgrowth of the midbrain. This means that it is connected by nervous tissue to the hypothalamus in the midbrain, and the hypothalamus exerts control over the posterior

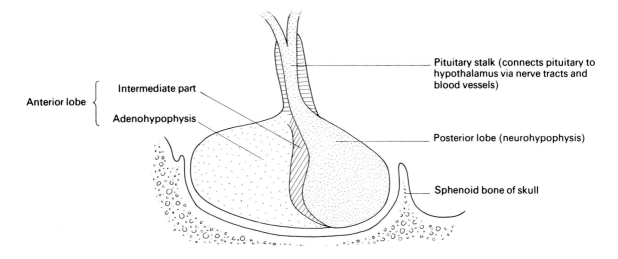

Labels on figure:
Anterior lobe { Intermediate part
Adenohypophysis

Pituitary stalk (connects pituitary to hypothalamus via nerve tracts and blood vessels)

Posterior lobe (neurohypophysis)

Sphenoid bone of skull

Figure 7.14 Vertical section of the pituitary body (hypophysis)

pituitary through nerves.

• The anterior lobe (*adenohypopphsis*) is formed from an upgrowth of the roof of the embryonic mouth cavity. It thus lacks nervous connection to the hypothalamus, although the two organs are still connected via blood vessels through the *pituitary stalk*. The hypothalamus can therefore exert control over the anterior pituitary via chemical releasing factors secreted into the blood.

The posterior pituitary releases two hormones:
• *Antidiuretic hormone (ADH)* affects water loss via the urine, and hence regulates blood osmolality (see page 62).
• *Oxytocin* alters the tone of smooth muscle. During the birth process, for example, it increases the tone of uterine smooth muscle, while lowering the tone of the cervical smooth muscle, making it possible for the baby to be born (see Chapter 8).

The synthesis of these two hormones occurs in neurone cell bodies in the hypothalamus. They then travel down the axons to the posterior pituitary where they can be released into the blood by *neurosecretion*.

The anterior pituitary secretes seven hormones, all under the influence of the hormonal–releasing factors from the hypothalamus. The hormones are known as tropic hormones (*tropos* meaning turning) as they 'turn on' other endocrine glands or processes.
• *Follicle stimulating hormone (FSH)* is a gonadotropin, secreted both in females and males. In females, FSH stimulates the development of ova and the secretion of oestrogens by the ovaries. In

males, FSH initiates sperm production in the testes.
• *Luteinising hormone (LH)*, another gonadotropin, stimulates ovulation in the ovary, and the subsequent formation of a corpus luteum that secretes progesterone. (The gonadotropins are dealt with more fully in Chapter 8.)
• *Prolactin* initiates and maintains milk production in the mammary glands (see page 113).
• *Thyroid stimulating hormone (TSH)* is a thyrotropin. It stimulates the synthesis and release of thyroxine (see page 96).
• *Adrenocorticotrophic hormone (ACTH)* controls the synthesis and release of some adrenal cortex hormones (see page 99).
• *Melanocyte stimulating hormone (MSH)* causes an increase in skin pigmentation by stimulating the dispersion of melanin pigments in melanocytes under the epidermis.
• *Growth hormones (GH)*, or somatotropins, stimulate growth by promoting protein synthesis, especially in the skeleton and striated muscles. It is therefore particularly important in young animals so that sufficient bone growth occurs before the growing regions (*epiphyseal cartilages*) ossify and close (see Fig.2.7(b)). It also stimulates the catabolic breakdown of glycogen and fat which can then be respired to provide energy for growth.

The release of GH is stimulated by *growth hormone releasing factor* and inhibited by *growth hormone inhibiting factor*, both from the hypothalamus. The releasing factor is produced in response to low blood concentrations of glucose and fatty acids, high blood amino acids, stress, and vigorous exercise, while the inhibiting factor is produced in response to increased blood concentrations of glucose and fatty acids, decreased blood amino acids, emotional deprivation, and obesity. If growth hormone is undersecreted during the growth years, then growth is slow and the growing regions ossify before the bones have reached full length. This condition is called *pituitary dwarfism* and its treatment requires regular injections of growth hormone while the patient is still young.

Q 18. Why must growth hormone (GH) treatment be given when young?

19. Why is the GH not administered by mouth?

20. GH has only recently become readily available. What new technique has allowed this?

21. GH is now given to cows on some farms to boost the milk yields, and it is released into the milk. Does this pose any risk to people who drink the milk?

■ The thyroid gland

The thyroid gland is situated on the neck just below the larynx. There are two lobes, one on either side of the trachea, connected to each other by a piece of thyroid tissue called the isthmus.

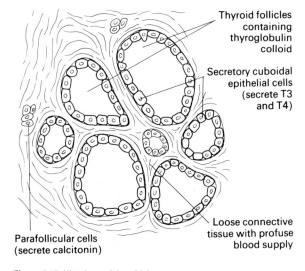

Thyroid follicles containing thyroglobulin colloid

Secretory cuboidal epithelial cells (secrete T3 and T4)

Loose connective tissue with profuse blood supply

Parafollicular cells (secrete calcitonin)

Figure 7.15 Histology of thyroid tissue

The parafollicular cells (which do not reach the follicle lumen) secrete the hormone, *calcitonin* (Fig.7.15). Calcitonin decreases blood calcium level by inhibiting bone breakdown and by accelerating calcium absorption by bones. It works in opposition to the parathyroid hormone, *parathormone*, which increases blood calcium levels.

Q 22. Which cells are responsible for bone breakdown, and which are responsible for the building up of bones?

The cells that border each follicle lumen synthesise the thyroid hormones, *thyroxine* (T4 for short as it contains four iodine atoms) and *tri-iodothyronine* (T3 for short as it contains three iodine atoms). These hormones perform similar functions, the main differences being that although more T4 is produced, T3 acts faster and with greater potency.

The follicular cells actively absorb *iodine* ions (iodide) from the blood, concentrating them up to 300 times the blood concentration. Iodide is then oxidised to iodine and this is linked to the amino acid *tyrosine*. Linkage occurs in the lumen of the follicle, within a large glycoprotein molecule called *thyroglobulin*, which can then store the hormones for months if necessary. When the hormones are required, thyroglobulin is absorbed by *pinocytosis* into the follicle cells. The thyroid hormones then diffuse into the blood where they bind to a plasma protein. This carries them to their target cells, ensuring that they remain in the blood and are not excreted.

The thyroid hormones are particularly concerned with the rate of chemical processes in the body, and they maintain the *basal metabolic rate (BMR)*. They stimulate the breakdown of carbohydrates and fats, causing increased production of heat by the body and so raising body temperature. In conjunction with pituitary growth hormone they stimulate protein synthesis, and hence help to regulate growth and development, especially in children. They can also increase the reactivity of the nervous system, resulting in increased frequency and force of heartbeat, raised blood pressure, increased peristalsis in the gut, and increased nervous energy.

If the metabolic rate is too low, iodine chemoreceptors in the hypothalamus sense the low concentration of thyroid hormones in the blood. The hypothalamus is stimulated to secrete

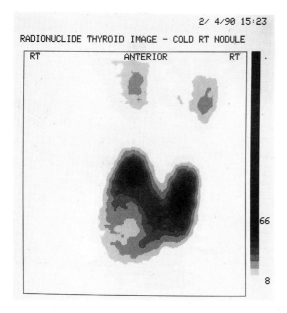

Shape of normal thyroid on ventral side of larynx

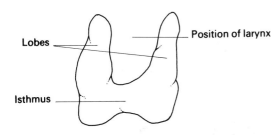

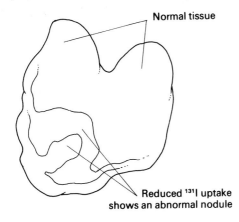

Figure 7.16 A gamma scan (above) of thyroid tissue. The normal dark tissue has taken up the radioactive iodine (^{131}I which emits gamma rays. The abnormal nodule has not and remains light (see diagram)

thyroptropin releasing factor (TRF) into the blood. This induces the anterior pituitary to release thyroid stimulating hormone (TSH), which increases the activity of the follicle cells in the thyroid. Providing T3 and T4 have been synthesised, the hormones are released into the blood, and the metabolic rate is restored to normal. This means that the iodine chemoreceptors will no longer be stimulated, so the release of TRF is switched off by negative feedback.

If too much TSH is present in the blood, the follicle cells will be overstimulated, resulting in the development of extra thyroid tissue. This appears as a swelling in the neck called a *goitre*. The extra tissue produces excess thyroid hormone, a condition known as *hyperthyroidism*. The metabolic rate increases, as does the pulse rate, ventilation rate and body temperature, and patients become nervous and excitable. They can be treated with drugs that inhibit thyroid hormone synthesis, or by the surgical removal of part of the gland.

If thyroid tissue is damaged, the uptake of iodine is impaired. This means that the distribution of normal and damaged tissue can be demonstrated by injecting a radioactive isotope of iodine into the bloodstream. Only the normal thyroid tissue will take up and use radioactive iodine. This emits gamma rays which can be photographed using a gamma camera. A gamma scan of thyroid tissue is shown in Fig.7.16.

Undersecretion of thyroid hormones results in *hypothyroidism*. In a child this leads to *cretinism*, while in an adult, thyroxine deficiency causes *myxoedema*.

Q 23. (a) From what you know about the functions of the thyroid hormones, suggest what symptoms might occur in cretinism, and in myxoedema. (b) How could these conditions be treated?

24. Goitre can also be caused by lack of iodine in the diet. Explain why this should stimulate the thyroid to become enlarged.

■ **Islets of Langerhans**
The pancreas contains several thousand *islets of Langerhans*, which are isolated clusters of endocrine cells embedded amongst the acini of the digestive part of the pancreas (see page 75).
The two main types of cell in an islet are the *beta*

Two patients, Claud who is 17 years old and Mary who is 20 years old and eight months pregnant, have both been found to have glucose in their urine. They attend their local hospital for glucose tolerance tests, to make sure they are not suffering from diabetes mellitis (due to lack of insulin). After fasting overnight their fasting blood glucose level is measured at the start, then they each take 50 grammes of glucose suspended in a decilitre of water. Their blood glucose levels are measured at half hour intervals for two and a half hours. The results were obtained as shown in Table 7.2.

 26. Are either Claud or Mary suffering from diabetes mellitus?

27. If one of them is not suffering from diabetes, what do you think could be causing the glucose loss in the urine?

28. What type of insulin do most sugar diabetics now use?

Name	Start (0h)	0.5 h	1 h	1.5 h	2 h	2.5 h
Claud	7.1	9.8	10.5	11.6	11.8	10.4
Mary	3.5	6.8	7.2	6.3	4.6	3.7

Table 7.2 Glucose levels (in millosmoles dm^{-3})

cells, which secrete insulin, and the *alpha cells*, which secrete *glucagon*. Both these hormones are small proteins.

• *Insulin* lowers blood glucose levels. It accelerates the facilitated uptake of glucose into cells, stimulates the conversion of glucose into the storage polymer glycogen, and inhibits the breakdown of glycogen to glucose. It also stimulates protein synthesis and fat synthesis.

• *Glucagon* raises blood glucose levels, by stimulating the breakdown of glycogen to glucose, and by stimulating the conversion of amino acids and glycerol into glucose.

 25. Where is glycogen stored in the body?

The release of insulin and glucagon is regulated by negative feedback control. When the blood glucose level drops *below* the norm, chemical receptors on the alpha cells of the islets stimulate the alpha cells to release glucagon. When the glucose level in the blood has risen back to the norm, these receptors are switched off and glucagon release stops. If the blood glucose level rises *above* the norm, this is sensed by receptors on the beta cells, and the beta cells are stimulated to release insulin. Insulin release is then switched off when the blood glucose level falls.

Other hormones in the body may also increase blood glucose level, e.g. pituitary growth hormone, and adrenaline. ACTH raises it by stimulating the secretion of glucocorticosteroid hormones from the adrenal cortex; and the gut wall hormones, gastrin, secretin and cholecystokinin, raise it by inhibiting insulin secretion.

The normal level of blood glucose after fasting for about ten hours, is 3.4 - 5.7 millimoles mm^{-3}. This represents the *respiratory level* of glucose, i.e. that amount being carried to the cells for metabolic needs. After a meal the level may rise to about 9.0 millimoles dm^{-3}, as glucose is absorbed from the gut more quickly than it is removed from the blood by liver cells and changed to glycogen. Glucose only appears in urine if the blood concentration exceeds 10 millimoles dm^{-3}. This is the *renal threshold*, at which so much glucose is passing into the glomerular filtrate that the active reabsorption mechanisms for glucose cannot cope.

■ **The adrenal bodies**
There are two adrenal glands which are small bodies which lie just anterior to the kidneys. Each gland has two distinct portions that function independently. A wide cortex to the outside, and a small medulla inside. Like other endocrine glands, the adrenals are extremely vascular (Fig.7.17).

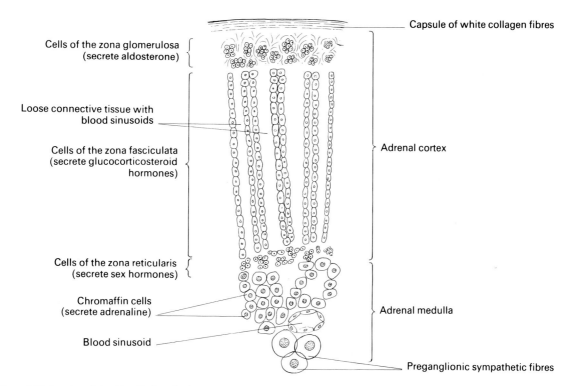

Cells of the zona glomerulosa
(secrete aldosterone)

Loose connective tissue with
blood sinusoids

Cells of the zona fasciculata
(secrete glucocorticosteroid
hormones)

Cells of the zona reticularis
(secrete sex hormones)

Chromaffin cells
(secrete adrenaline)

Blood sinusoid

Capsule of white collagen fibres

Adrenal cortex

Adrenal medulla

Preganglionic sympathetic fibres

Figure 7.17 An adrenal gland (vertical section)

• The *adrenal cortex* contains rounded groups of cells (zona glomerulosa) that secrete mineralo-corticosteroid hormones, and columns of cells either in bundles (zona fasciculata) or scattered (zona reticularis) that secrete glucocorticosteroid hormones and minute amounts of steroid sex hormones respectively.

The most important mineralocorticoid is *aldosterone*, which increases the uptake of sodium ions by the kidney (see page 62).

The most important glucocorticoids are *cortisol* and *cortisone*. These promote the breakdown (*catabolism*) of proteins, fatty acids and glycogen, and cause the synthesis of glucose from amino acids if blood glucose levels are low. They also provide resistance to stress, and are anti-inflammatory. The release of glucocorticoids is controlled by negative feedback. Various types of stress, or a low glucocorticoid level in the blood, induce the hypothalamus to release *corticotropin releasing factor (CRF)*. This stimulates the anterior pituitary to release *adrenocorticotrophic hormone (ACTH)* into the blood, which targets onto the zona fasciculata causing the release of cortisol and cortisone. As the blood concentration of these rises, the release of CRF is damped.

Q 29. Sleep also induces the release of CRF by the hypothalamus. Does this mean that sleeping is a stressful activity? What other explanation could there be?

• The *adrenal medulla* is really an extension of the sympathetic nervous system. The cells are probably modified postganglionic sympathetic neurones that have become specialised to secrete the hormones, *adrenaline* and *noradrenaline*, both of which mimic the sympathetic nervous system in their effects. Adrenaline is more potent than noradrenaline, otherwise their effects are similar, producing the following 'fight, flight, or frolic' responses to stressful situations. The both increase cardiac output and blood pressure, and raise the glucose level in the blood. They divert blood to where it is most needed, by causing vasoconstriction of vessels to the skin and gut, and vasodilation of vessels to the striated muscles and brain. They also improve ventilation, dilate the pupils and increase mental awareness.

REPRODUCTION, GROWTH AND DEVELOPMENT

■ CASE STUDY: A TEST TUBE BABY

At least one in eight couples in the UK suffer from infertility, and John and Deborah were one of them. Four years after their marriage, Deborah had still not conceived, so they went for tests at their local infertility clinic. A sample of John's semen turned out to be perfectly adequate, but it appeared that both of Deborah's oviducts were blocked. She was ovulating normally, but neither eggs nor sperm were able to pass through the oviducts for fertilisation. The damage was too severe for surgical correction, so the only way John and Deborah could have a baby would be by '*in vitro*' *fertilisation (IVF)* and *embryo implantation*.

In vitro fertilisation literally means 'fertilisation in glass', in other words, outside the body. IVF was first carried out successfully in 1959, by Dr M. C. Chang, using rabbit gametes. In vitro fertilisation of human gametes was achieved in 1969 by Dr Steptoe, Dr Edwards and Dr Bavister, although a successful implantation of the embryo in the mother's uterus took another nine years. The first 'test tube' baby was born in 1978.

Deborah was given hormones to increase her egg production, and her ovaries were observed by ultrasound scanning to detect when they were ready to ovulate (release the eggs). She was then given a local anaesthetic, and the doctor was able to collect six eggs using a fine tube inserted via the vagina. The eggs were maintained in a suitable culture medium in an incubator while John's semen sample was separated into sperm and seminal fluid by centrifugation. The sample contained about 500 million sperm, of which about a fifth were added to the eggs. If fertilisation occurs, the embryo is kept for two more days in culture until it has reached the four cell stage. It can then be transplanted into the mother's uterus, where it may or may not become implanted. The success rate for this technique is still less than 10%, but luckily Deborah became pregnant, and she and John are now the proud parents of a little boy.

Q 1. The IVF technique often means that more eggs are fertilised than can be implanted. This means that human embryos are available for study and experimentation. Many people are strongly opposed to this. Can you suggest one reason for allowing this type of research to take place, and one reason why it should not be allowed.

■ HUMAN REPRODUCTIVE SYSTEMS

■ The male reproductive system

Study Fig.8.1 which shows the anatomy of the male genital system. The male gonads are the *testes*. They are formed in the abdomen but before birth they descend from the abdominal cavity through the inguinal rings (a passageway between the abdominal wall muscles) into the *scrotal sacs*. The scrotal sacs hang outside the body and this helps to keep the testes cool enough for sperm production. The blood vessels of the testes also act as a heat exchange system. Veins draining blood from the testes coil around the supplying arteries, and as the venous blood has been cooled in the scrotum, the arterial blood is also cooled.

The testes contain hormone-secreting interstitial cells between the seminiferous tubules, and these cells secrete male hormones, such as *testosterone*, into the bloodstream. The seminiferous tubules become active after puberty, producing *sperm* by the process of *spermatogenesis*. Sperm cells pass first into the *epididymis*, where they may be stored or reabsorbed if necessary, and then through the *vas deferens* during ejaculation. Secretions from

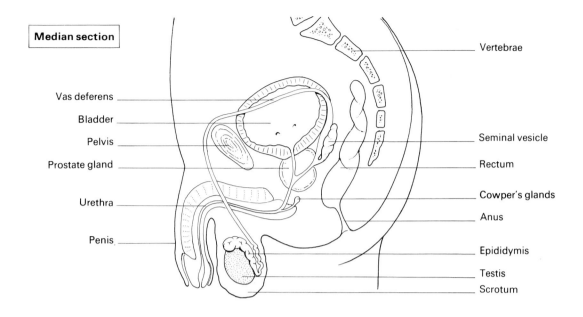

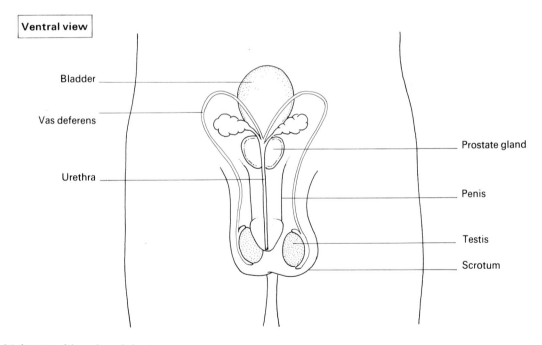

Figure 8.1 Anatomy of the male genital system

the *prostate gland* and *seminal vesicles* are poured on to the sperm near where the left and right vasa deferentia join, and the *Cowper's glands* add their secretions in the urethra. The semen, or seminal fluid, is now complete.

The *penis* becomes erect due to raised blood pressure during sexual excitement as the arteries dilate and veins constrict. It can then be inserted into the female vagina, where semen is released through the male urethra during ejaculation.

■ The female reproductive system

Study Fig.8.2 which shows the anatomy of the female genital system. The female gonads are the *ovaries*, which lie in the abdominal cavity and are responsible for producing both gametes and hormones. In humans, usually only one gamete (ovum) matures each month at *ovulation*, it is released into the ovarian funnel and so into the fallopian tube (*oviduct*) leading to the uterus. If copulation has occurred, the ovum may be fertilised by sperm from the male in the oviduct. The resulting embryo develops in the uterus throughout pregnancy.

The *cervix* is the entrance to the uterus. It allows semen to enter during or after copulation, and allows the shed lining of the uterus (*endometrium*) to leave during menstruation. It is normally very narrow to reduce the chances of uterine infection, but widens at birth to allow the baby to pass through. The *vagina* receives the penis during intercourse.

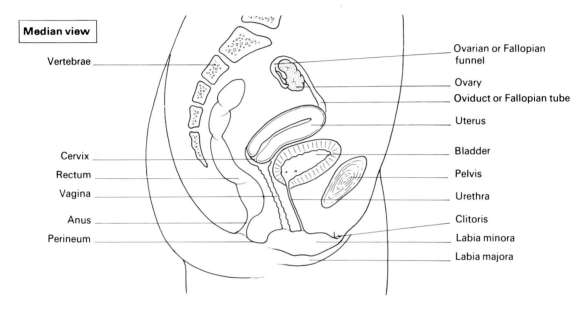

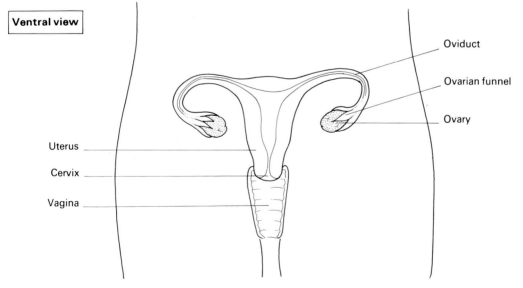

Figure 8.2 Anatomy of the female genital system

■ GAMETE DEVELOPMENT

Gametogenesis is the formation of gametes; spermatogenesis in the male and oogenesis in the female

■ Formation of male gametes

Spermatogenesis occurs in the *seminiferous tubules* of the testis (Fig.8.3). Each testis is divided into about 250 lobules, each of which can contain up to four highly coiled seminiferous tubules giving a huge surface area for sperm production. The heat generated by this process would actually kill the sperm as they are formed if the structure of the testes and their position in the scrotal sacs did not favour cooling. The seminiferous tubules become active at puberty under the control of the sex hormone, FSH, from the anterior pituitary body (see page 95), and spermatogenesis can then occur continually throughout a man's life.

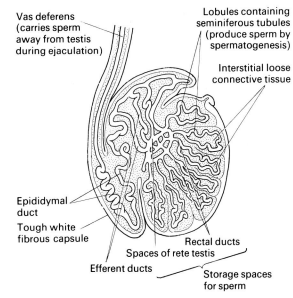

Figure 8.3 (a) Internal structure of the testis and epididymis

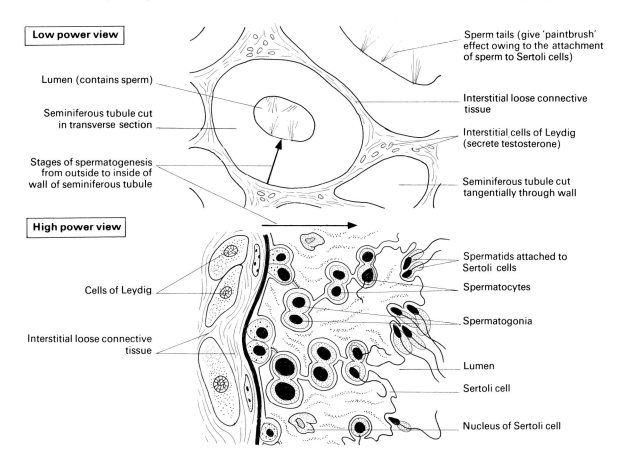

Figure 8.3 (b) Histology of testis tissue (under low and high power view)

The process of spermatogenesis (Fig.8.4) takes about three weeks. The seminiferous tubules are lined with cells called *spermatogonia* (sperm mother cells). These divide actively by *mitosis* to produce *diploid* daughter spermatogonia, which will eventually form spermatozoa, and more sperm mother cells to act as a reserve for further spermatogenesis. Millions of daughter spermatogonia are formed and new ones push older ones away from the basement membrane towards the lumen of the seminiferous tubule. The older ones have by now enlarged slightly to become diploid *primary spermatocytes*, which then undergo *meiosis* to become *haploid*. This first meiotic division produces two *secondary spermatocytes* per primary spermatocyte and these each divide into two *spermatids* by the second meiotic division. The heads of the haploid spermatids then embed in *Sertoli cells* in the walls of the seminiferous tubules for further development into mature *spermatozoa* (Fig.8.5) The Sertoli cells support and probably nourish the spermatozoa. Spermatozoa can be stored in the epididymis and vas deferens for several months, and if not ejaculated they are eventually reabsorbed.

Q 2. Give two reasons why meiosis is important in gametogenesis.

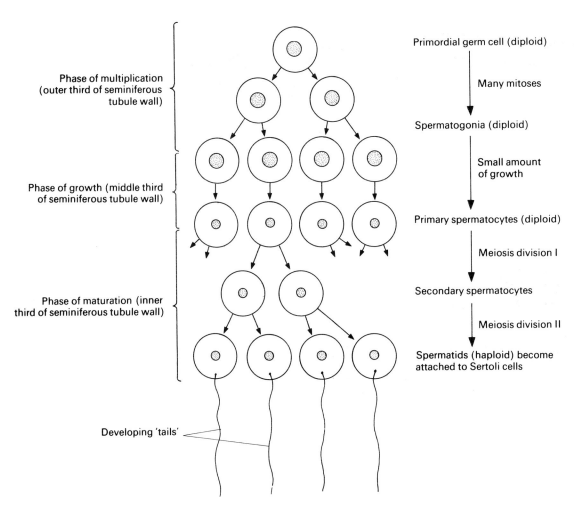

Figure 8.4 The process of spermatogenesis

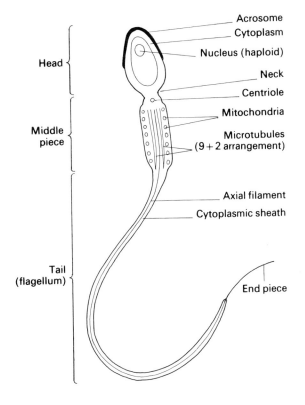

Figure 8.5 Mature spermatazoan

■ Formation of female gametes

Oogenesis begins in the ovary (Fig.8.6) of the fetus. A germinal epithelium of egg mother cells is on the outside of the fetal ovary. The egg mother cell divides repeatedly by *mitosis* to form diploid *oogonia*, which migrate into the connective tissue mass within the ovary. Each oogonium is surrounded by a layer of epithelium cells, forming a *primary follicle*, and these remain dormant until puberty. At birth there are about 400 000 oogonia in the two ovaries.

From puberty onwards the completion of oogenesis (Fig.8.7) occurs within the 'context' of the *menstrual cycle*. Three or four oogonia per month are stimulated by FSH to synthesise more cytoplasm and yolk (food store). Their size increases considerably, and they are termed *primary oocytes*. At the same time, the primary follicle develops into a mature ovarian follicle (*Graafian follicle*), in which the follicle becomes hollow, and the epithelial cells multiply to form a multi-layered coat which secretes the female hormone *oestrogen*.

Eventually one of the follicles bulges out of the ovary surface and ruptures (*ovulation*), releasing the oocyte to the ovarian funnel. Degeneration of any remaining developing follicles in the ovary

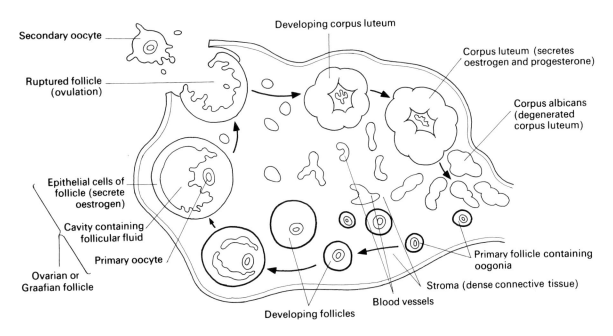

Figure 8.6 Histology of the ovary. These structures would not be seen in an ovary at the same time, but are shown here, in sequence, to demonstrate the monthly menstrual cycle

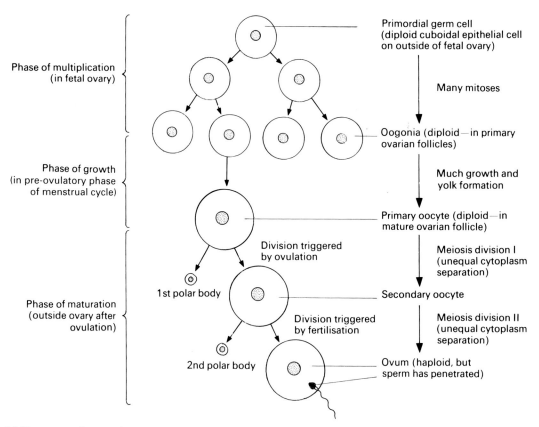

Figure 8.7 The process of oogenesis

Phase of multiplication
(in fetal ovary)

Phase of growth
(in pre-ovulatory phase
of menstrual cycle)

Phase of maturation
(outside ovary after
ovulation)

Primordial germ cell
(diploid cuboidal epithelial cell
on outside of fetal ovary)

Many mitoses

Oogonia (diploid—in primary
ovarian follicles)

Much growth and
yolk formation

Primary oocyte (diploid—in
mature ovarian follicle)

Division triggered
by ovulation

1st polar body

Meiosis division I
(unequal cytoplasm
separation)

Secondary oocyte

Division triggered
by fertilisation

Meiosis division II
(unequal cytoplasm
separation)

2nd polar body

Ovum (haploid, but
sperm has penetrated)

then occurs. The first meiotic division takes place at ovulation and the primary oocyte becomes a secondary *oocyte*. Meiosis II will only occur if the secondary oocyte is penetrated by a sperm head, i.e. fertilised, in the oviduct. The process of meiosis in oogenesis is unusual. There is equal *nuclear* division, producing two and then four haploid nuclei, but cytoplasmic division is very unequal, most of the cytoplasm going to the potential ovum, with very little left for the tiny first and second polar bodies. Unfortunately, in Deborah's case (page 100), oogenesis could not be completed as the sperm and secondary oocyte couldn't meet owing to her blocked oviducts.

The ovum (secondary oocyte) must be fertilised within 24 hours after ovultation or it dies. A fertilised ovum (Fig.8.8) is then wafted by ciliary action along the oviduct to the uterus. This takes 3-4 days during which time *cleavage* begins, and a ball of cells called an embryo is formed. The embryo may then implant into the glandular lining (*endometrium*) of the uterus.

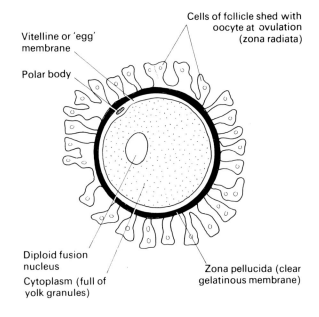

Cells of follicle shed with
oocyte at ovulation
(zona radiata)

Vitelline or 'egg'
membrane

Polar body

Diploid fusion
nucleus

Cytoplasm (full of
yolk granules)

Zona pellucida (clear
gelatinous membrane)

Figure 8.8 Fertilised ovum

■ The menstrual cycle

The menstrual or monthly female cycle begins at puberty (at approximately 13 years old) when the anterior pituitary starts secreting large amounts of gonadotropic hormones (see page 95). These regulate the events of the menstrual cycle, and are themselves regulated by releasing factors from the hypothalamus, and by ovarian hormones via negative feedback.

The menstrual cycle (Fig.8.9) and onset of puberty in the female depends initially on the secretion of gonadotropin releasing factor (GnRF) by the hypothalamus. This triggers the release of FSH from the anterior pituitary gland. FSH stimulates the development of primary follicles into ovarian follicles, and also causes the secretion of oestrogens by the follicles. *Oestrogens* promote the healing and repair of the uterus lining after

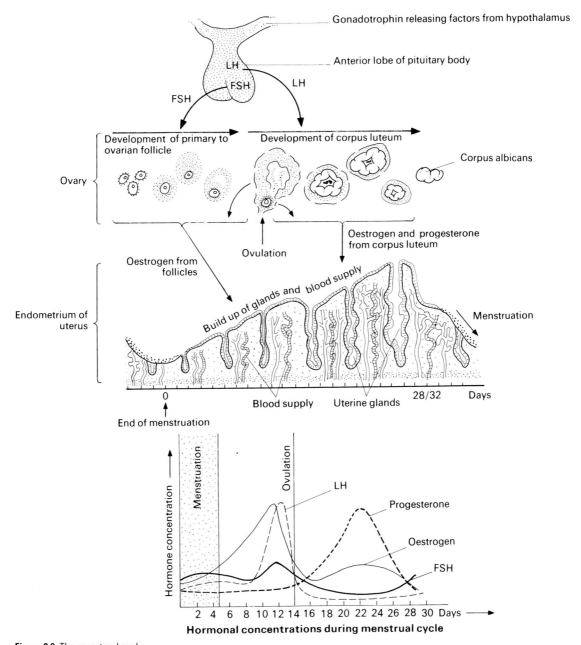

Figure 8.9 The menstrual cycle

menstruation, and more generally, they cause the development and maintenance of the female secondary sexual characteristics (which include fat distribution to the breasts and hips, a broader pelvis, a high pitched voice, and the growth of public hair).

Q 3. The development of secondary sexual characteristics in men is promoted by the male hormone testosterone. What are these characteristics?

High oestrogen levels in the blood around the time of ovulation have two effects. Firstly, they inhibit the release of GnRF, and hence of FSH, by negative feedback (which is why oestrogen-type contraceptive pills are effective). Secondly, they cause the anterior pituitary to release increasing amounts of *luteinising hormone (LH)* by positive feedback.

LH stimulates ovulation, in which the ovarian follicle ruptures to release the secondary oocyte into the ovarian funnel. It also causes the remains of the follicle to develop into a *corpus luteum* ('yellow body') which starts to release *progesterone*. Oestrogen and progesterone together maintain and cause further development of the endometrium and breasts.

If fertilisation does not occur, the rising levels of these hormones inhibit the secretion of GnRF and LH. The corpus luteum is therefore allowed to degenerate, becoming a small white fibrous *corpus albicans* ('white body'). Thus the concentrations of oestrogen and progesterone fall and their maintaining action on the endometrium is lost. The subsequent breakdown of the endometrium results in the menstrual flow of blood and cells to the exterior through the vagina. Menstruation lasts for 3-5 days and then a new monthly cycle commences. The hormonal events that occur if pregnancy occurs will be described later.

■ FROM GAMETES TO EMBRYO

■ Copulation
For fertilisation to occur male sperm must first be introduced into the female vagina by the penis during sexual intercourse. Sexual excitement in the male triggers impulses from the cerebrum via *parasympathetic* nerves, which cause the erectile tissue within the penis to become engorged with blood, so the penis becomes stiff and erect. At the same time, parasympathetic impulses cause the Cowper's glands to secrete mucus into the urethra for lubrication.

When the penis is in the vagina, tactile stimuli eventually result in the emission of semen (*ejaculation*), a process that is under *sympathetic* control. Impulses cause peristaltic waves in the smooth muscle of the epididymis, vas deferens and seminal ducts that propel sperm into the urethra. The seminal vesicles and prostate glands contract to expel fluids onto the sperm, and the semen thus formed is forcibly ejected from the male's urethra into the vagina. This sensation is called *orgasm*, and a similar sensation may be experienced by the female. The clitoris (homologous to the penis) becomes erect, mucus is secreted by vestibular glands into the vagina, and the muscular spasms of the vagina, uterus and oviducts help to propel semen up to the oviducts.

■ Fertilisation
Fertilisation is the fusion of haploid male and female gametes to form a diploid *zygote*, the first cell of the new generation. It usually occurs high up in the oviduct, during the first 24 hours after ovulation. Contractions of the uterus and oviduct may convey sperm to the oocyte in minutes, but the sperm remain incapable of fertilisation for about six hours. During this time the tip of the sperm (*acrosome*) has to synthesise *hyaluronidase* and other enzymes, such as *proteases*, to dissolve the intercellular materials and remaining follicle cells surrounding the oocyte.

A receptor on the acrosome then attaches to a specific receptor on the egg (*vitelline*) membrane. The acrosome membrane ruptures, releasing hyaluronidase which softens the vitelline membrane at the point of contact. Meanwhile the membrane lining the acrosome appears to turn inside out, forming a thin filament that penetrates the egg membrane, allowing the whole sperm (in humans) to enter. This process is called the *acrosome reaction*.

Penetration by a sperm triggers the completion of meiosis II so that the oocyte becomes a true ovum. The two haploid nuclei fuse to become a diploid segmentation nucleus, with 23 chromosomes from the female and 23 chromosomes from the male. The entry of further sperm is prevented by the *cortical reaction* in the cortex, (outer region) of the ovum. In this process receptor sites on the vitelline membrane are altered by enzymes from the fertilised ovum, and the cortical cytoplasm is thickened by the migration of fat and protein granules to the area.

Q 4. Artificial insemination has been used for many years in cattle breeding. What do you think 'artificial insemination' means, and what advantages do you think it has?

■ Cleavage
Immediately after fertilisation, the zygote starts to divide rapidly by mitosis. The number of cells increases although the overall size does not, so the *zona pellucida* and *corona radiata* remain intact for a while. This process of cleavage is progressing while the dividing zygote (early embryo) is being moved along the oviduct to the uterus (Fig.8.10).

The first cleavage, to a two cell stage, takes about 36 hours, but each successive mitosis takes less time to complete. After 48 hours four cells are present, and after 72 hours, 16 cells. A few days after fertilisation there is a solid ball of tiny cells (*blastomeres*). The ball is termed a *morula* (meaning mulberry), and it is still only the size of the original zygote. This development has all been at the expense of the small yolk food store within the zygote and offspring cells.

Further division results in the morula becoming a hollow ball of cells called a *blastocyst* which arrives in the uterus. The blastomeres round the outside form the *trophoblast*, or 'feeding' layer. There is a mass of smaller cells at one end, called the *embryonal knob*, which will eventually form the *embryo*. The trophoblast can absorb nutrients from the 'uterine milk' secreted by the endometrial glands of the uterus lining. Absorption of these nutrients occurs by diffusion, osmosis, facilitated and active transport, and by pinocytosis.

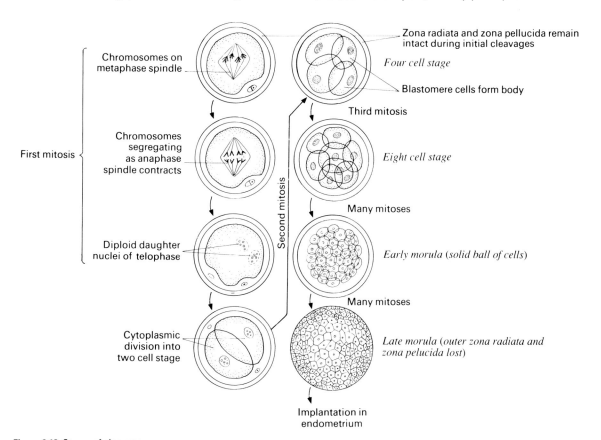

Figure 8.10 Stages of cleavage

■ Implantation

Implantation follows seven or eight days after fertilisation, and usually occurs in a part of the uterus away from the cervix. The blastocyst (*embryo*) is now about 0.22 mm in diameter, and the corona radiata and zona pellucida have been lost. The trophoblast cells secrete enzymes that digest part of the endometrium enabling the embryo to burrow completely into the spongy, glandular tissue of the uterine wall.

 5. What difficulties would occur if the embryo implanted near the cervix?

■ GESTATION/PREGNANCY

The *gestation period* lasts from fertilisation to birth, while *pregnancy* is usually only deemed to have begun once the embryo is successfully implanted. On the other hand, while the gestation period for humans is about 38 weeks, the pregnancy is 40 weeks, and includes the two weeks before gestation begins.

The first two months of the gestation period are usually termed the *embryonic period*. This is the time when the rudiments of the main organ systems are developed and the fetal membranes are formed. Once the placenta is developed and functioning, the embryo is no longer dependent on trophoblastic nutrition and 'uterine milk'. The developing organism is then called a fetus and enters the *fetal period* of development.

■ Embryonic development

After implantation, the embryonal knob differentiates into the three primary germ layers, ectoderm, endoderm and mesoderm. This process is called *gastrulation* and occurs very rapidly in humans so that it is difficult to establish a clear course of events.

The ectoderm on the outside gives rise to the skin and nervous system of the embryo, while the endoderm on the inside forms the lining of the gut and secretory portions of the liver and pancreas. The mesoderm in the middle forms the skeleton and connective tissues, the blood and blood system, smooth muscle, skeletal muscle and caridac muscle.

There are four fetal membranes, the *chorion*, the *splanchnopleure* (around the yolk sac), the *amnion* (enclosing the amniotic cavity) and the *allantois* (Fig.8.11). The amnion is a thin membrane that eventually surrounds the fetus completely. It becomes filled with *amniotic fluid*, which acts as a 'shock absorber' to protect the fetus, and also enables the fetus to move and exercise its developing muscles. The splanchnopleure is largely non-functional in mammals, since the embryo relies on 'uterine milk' during early development, not on a huge yolk supply.

The chorion surrounds the fetus and all the other membranes, and is derived from the trophoblast layer and mesoderm, while the allantois grows out from the hindgut of the fetus. The chorion and allantois fuse to form a vascular structure called an allantochorion, which makes up the fetal part of the *placenta*.

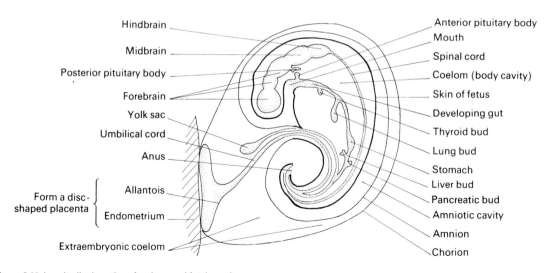

Hindbrain
Midbrain
Posterior pituitary body
Forebrain
Yolk sac
Umbilical cord
Anus
Form a disc-shaped placenta { Allantois
Endometrium
Extraembryonic coelom

Anterior pituitary body
Mouth
Spinal cord
Coelom (body cavity)
Skin of fetus
Developing gut
Thyroid bud
Lung bud
Stomach
Liver bud
Pancreatic bud
Amniotic cavity
Amnion
Chorion

Figure 8.11 Longitudinal section of embryo and fetal membranes

■ CASE STUDY: ULTRASOUND SCANNING AND AMNIOCENTESIS

Mrs Thomas was 44 when her third pregnancy was confirmed. She already had the ten-year-old twins, Sophie and Julie, plus William aged four who has Down's syndrome (trisomy 21 - three copies of Chromosome 21). Despite some handicap, William is a happy and healthy boy, and with modern medical care and education, he can expect to have a full happy life. The risk of genetic disease does increase in older mothers, however, so it was decided that Mrs Thomas should be 'screened' for a number of genetic disorders. If her fetus was seriously abnormal, she would be given the option of terminating her pregnancy by abortion.

In an *ultrascan* (see below), high frequency ultrasound waves are directed on to the abdomen of the expectant mother (this is quite harmless whereas X-rays would be dangerous). The ultrasound waves are reflected off the various surfaces through the abdomen and can be collected by a transducer into a recorder which gives a visual picture of what is inside the abdomen and uterus. Physical defects such as spina bifida or microcephaly, may be visible in the fetus. The doctor can also locate the amniotic cavity and use a hypodermic needle to withdraw some amniotic fluid from it without touching the fetus. Embryonic cells in the fluid are then examined for biochemical defects and also for abnormalities in chromosome number or structure. This procedure is called *amniocentesis*, and can diagnose about 350 different fetal defects, a number of which are life threatening and may justify abortion. Haemophilia, muscular dystrophy, cystic fibrosis, Down's syndrome, Turner's syndrome, Klinefelter's syndrome, myelocytic leukaemia, sickle cell anaemia and thalassaemia are among the 350 conditions which can be diagnosed.

Fortunately for Mr and Mrs Thomas the fetus appeared to be perfectly normal. The rest of the pregnancy went well and some months later, baby Rachel was born.

Q 6. If Mrs Thomas had been offered amniocentesis when she was pregnant with William, what difference would have been seen in the embryonic cells?

7. Sophie and Julie are identical twins. Did they develop from one egg or two, and from one sperm or two?

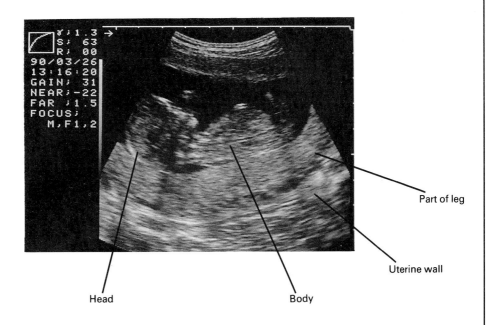

Head

Body

Part of leg

Uterine wall

Ultrasound scan of a 13 week old fetus in the womb

■ The placenta

The placenta is a vascular structure that develops from the allantois, chorion, and thickened endometrium of the uterus. It is fully formed by the third month of pregnancy, and provides the vital exchange surface between the maternal and fetal blood.

The chorion develops *chorionic villi* which push into the endometrium. The villi contain capillaries of the allantois and are directly bathed with maternal blood, forming a huge exchange surface area. Oxygen and nutrients diffuse from maternal to fetal blood and waste fetal products diffuse in the opposite direction. The blood does not actually mix however, except to a small degree as the placenta ages. The consequences of this were discussed in the context of rhesus blood groups (see page 19).

 8. How is oxygen off-loaded from the mother's blood into the fetal blood?

The other major function of the placenta is that it secretes hormones. These include oestrogens, human chorionic gonadotropin (HCG), placental luteotropic releasing factor (pLRF), human chorionic somatomammotropin (HCS), progesterone, and relaxin.

■ Fetal circulation

The fetus is attached to the placenta by the *umbilical cord*, which contains two arteries and a vein. The *umbilical arteries* are extensions of the internal iliac arteries of the fetus, and they will be blocked off when the umbilical cord is tied and cut at birth. The *umbilical vein* carries blood rich in nutrients and oxygen from the placenta to the fetal liver. Here there is a shunt vessel, called the *ductus venosus*, that bypasses the liver and transfers blood directly into the posterior vena cava.

This blood is carried to the right atrium, where there are two more shunts designed to bypass the pulmonary circulation. Clearly the lungs are not yet working so the pulmonary circulation is reduced, and it is important that the oxygen and nutrients in the blood reach the aorta as quickly as possible so that they can be conveyed to the body organs. The first shunt is the *foramen ovale*, a hole in the atrial septum of the fetus that allows blood to flow directly from the right atrium to the left atrium. The second shunt is a short vessel called the *ductus*

arteriosus that links the pulmonary arch to the aorta.

When the baby is born and takes its first breath, the pulmonary vessels expand, drawing blood into the pulmonary system. This equalises the blood pressures in the atria and arches, and thus causes the foramen ovale and ductus arteriosus to become blocked physiologically. A few days after the birth, they should also become blocked physically, as fibrous connective tissue grows across them. Occasionally the foramen ovale remains partly open, a defect known as a 'hole in the heart', and surgery may be necessary to close it.

■ The hormones of pregnancy

In normal menstrual cycles, either the oocyte is not fertilised, or a developing embryo fails to implant, so the corpus luteum degenerates. If there is successful implantation however, then the corpus luteum persists, and the output of oestrogen and progesterone is continued. These hormones maintain the lining of the endometrium throughout pregnancy, cause the further development of the myometrium (uterine smooth muscle) and prepare the mammary glands for later milk secretion. Progesterone also inhibits uterine smooth muscle from contracting, so high levels of this hormone prevent spontaneous abortion.

The trophoblast, and later the chorion, start secreting human chorionic gonadotropin (HCG). Most home pregnancy tests are designed to detect this as it is usually present in the urine of pregnant woman from about eight days after fertilisation. HCG increases in concentration up to the eighth week or so of pregnancy and then its concentration is greatly reduced. Its function is to take over from LH in maintaining the corpus luteum, so in effect it also maintains the pregnancy. By the fourth month the placenta itself is secreting oestrogen and progesterone, so HCG concentration falls as the corpus luteum is no longer required.

The other hormones secreted by the placenta are placental luteotropic releasing factor (pLRF), human chorionic somatomammotropin (HCS), and relaxin.
• pLRF stimulates the placenta to secrete HCG. It is similar chemically to GnRF from the hypothalamus of the mother, which regulates FSH and LH secretion (see page 95).
• HCS stimulates the development of breast tissue in the mother for lactation, and causes reduced use

of glucose in the mother, thus making it more available to the fetus. It also stimulates protein synthesis in the fetus and so promotes growth. The rate of HCS secretion increases in proportion to the increase in placental mass, reaching a maximum at 32 weeks and then remaining constant.

• Relaxin causes the ligaments of the pelvis, pubic symphysis and the sacro-iliac joints to relax or soften. This allows the pelvic canal to be widened to accommodate the baby during the birth process. Relaxin also stimulates the dilation of the cervical smooth muscle during birth, so that the baby may be expelled.

At about 36 weeks the placenta starts to age. Its hormone production is reduced, and its efficiency as a metabolite exchanger becomes impaired. Placental ageing and its results eventually triggers the birth process.

■ BIRTH AND BEYOND

■ Parturition, or birth

Birth is triggered by a complicated interaction of many factors that may occur as a result of *placental ageing* towards the end of the gestation period. The fetus may, for example, suffer *anoxia* (lack of oxygen), causing it to struggle and kick, and so stimulate the endometrial surface. This acts on the hypothalamus by direct nervous stimulation, initiating the release of ocytocin from the posterior pituitary body. Other factors include the fall of progesterone secretion by the placenta, which may enable uterine contractions to commence as progesterone inhibition is reduced; and the release of prostaglandin hormones from the placenta to induce labour.

The onset of labour is marked by the start of regular uterine contractions. These are made possible by the reduction in progesterone concentration, and are stimulated by a rising level of oxytocin (under positive feedback control) in the blood. True labour begins when the contractions are strong enough to become painful, and can be divided into three phases:

• In the *first stage of labour* there are regular contractions of the uterus, which increase in force and intensity. The amnion ruptures so that the amniotic fluid leaks out of the vagina, and the cervix dilates, up to about 10 cm diameter.

 9. What will happen to the oxytocin levels and to the uterine contractions once the amnion is ruptured? Why?

• In the *second stage of labour*, forcible contractions of the uterine smooth muscle force the baby head first (normally) through the cervix and vagina, or birth canal into the outside world. The umbilical cord is tied off and cut, and the baby is made to take its first breath. At this moment the fetal circulation is modified into the adult circulation.

• The *third stage of labour* is when powerful uterine contractions expel the placenta, or afterbirth, from the uterus. The high level of oxytocin in the blood causes vasoconstriction of the uterine blood vessels to curtail bleeding of the damaged endometrium.

■ Lactation

Lactation is the secretion and ejection of milk by the *mammary glands*. The main hormone involved in promoting milk synthesis by the secretory cells of the breasts is *prolactin* from the anterior pituitary gland. This is released in response to *prolactin releasing factor* (PRF) from the hypothalamus, which can only be secreted in low oestrogen and progesterone concentrations such as are encountered after birth. The high levels of these hormones during pregnancy stimulate the hypothalamus to release *prolactin inhibiting factor* (PIF).

The release of PRF is actually stimulated by the continual *suckling* actions of the infant on the mother's nipples, and this suckling also causes the hypothalamus to initiate the release of oxytocin from the posterior pituitary body. Oxytocin stimulates smooth muscle cells around the secretory alveoli of the mammary gland to contract, expelling milk into the milk reservoirs and milk ducts, and also stimulates the smooth muscle of these ducts to contract high up and relax near the nipple, so the milk can be obtained by the suckling infant.

The first milk that is secreted is called *colostrum*. This has a thick cloudy appearance, and although it contains less fat and milk sugar than normal milk, it is essential for the baby as it transfers *maternal antibodies* that can give the baby passive immunity for a few weeks.

10. What do you think are the advantages of breast feeding?

11. What would be the significance of a newborn baby being found to be HIV positive?

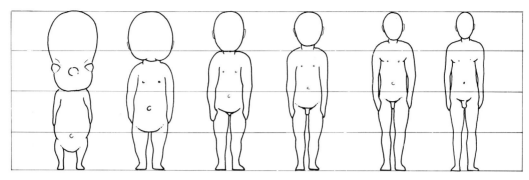

Figure 8.12 Changes in the proportions of human body parts owing to allometric growth

■ Postnatal growth

After birth the baby grows by *allometric growth* (Fig.8.12). This means that different organs in the body grow at different rates. The head of a newborn baby seems huge in proportion to the rest of its body, but the rest of the body grows more quickly than the head during the formative years, until the usual adult proportions are achieved.

■ Development and transitions

In the early stages of life there is total dependancy on the parents for food and protection. Some mammals are born more capable of fending for themselves than humans' young, and can stand and run about almost at once. At birth, the human baby is at an early stage of development and needs parental care for years of growth (i.e a permanent increase in biomass) and development (i.e changes in anatomy and physiology in maturation to adult form).

The major changes in a lifetime; birth, adolescence, menopause and death, are marked by biological and social transitions. Other events, such as starting school, accidental injury, starting a new job, marriage, are personal transitions unrelated to biological change. The first irreversible biological transition 'from the womb to the world' puts the baby at greater risk of death than any other 24 hours in its lifetime. The most rapid period of growth is the first two years of life and the next most rapid is the adolescent 'growth spurt' associated with puberty. This is the time when changes occur in the external appearance and biological function which enable the person to produce fertile eggs or sperms and to reproduce.

The spontaneous changes linked with growth and development can cause anxieties based on differences in the timing and magnitude of the change. In humans a great range in development

time is normal; so that although the average age at which menstruation starts in girls in the UK is 13.5, the normal range is from 10 to 16 (and there are frequent examples outside this range). Pubic hair may begin to grow in boys at any age between 10 and 15 (and in girls between 8 and 14). What is clear in this variation is that biological maturity is earlier in girls than in boys.

There are also geographical differences, and the trend is also towards earlier maturing: the average menarche (first menstruation) in the UK was 16 years of age in 1850 compared to 13.5 in 1970).

The final changes in the life of individuals are linked with ageing. Some body cells (blood and skin) age over a period of weeks and are rapidly replaced. Other cells age over the lifetime of the individual and may not be replaced (nerve cells in the brain and muscle). It is estimated that, between the ages of 30 and 90 years, cell loss accounts for a reduction of 50% of the nephrons and a change in the brain mass from an average of 1.5 kg to 1.36 kg. Changes in collagen levels result in wrinkles in the skin, brittle bones and deterioration in the lens of the eye. Degenerative changes in the arteries cause coronary heart disease and strokes. With ageing, cell division is also disrupted so that some cancers have an increased incidence. Women in the UK live an average of six years longer than men.

All growth and development depends on the environment, health and nutrition of the individual as well as on the anatomical and physiological characteristics inherited. In general, it is true to say that better living conditions support better health and a longer life. There are huge differences between the developing and the developed world. The expectation of life at birth is about 45 years in Bangladesh, Sierra Leone and Bolivia but well over 70 in Japan, USA and UK.

EXAMINATION QUESTIONS

A number of questions have been asked in the text of this book and most of them are of the type that could be set as part of an advanced examination. Some questions that have actually appeared in recent examinations now follow.

1. Discuss the concept of feedback control in relation to the maintenance of blood glucose level and water balance in the human body. (20)
(*London AS, 1990*)

2. (a) State the exact position of the pancreas in the body of a named mammal. (2)
(b) Describe the functions of the pancreatic secretions (glucagon not required). (12)
(c) Explain how the release of pancreatic secretions is controlled. (4)
(*Cambridge International A, 1990*)

3. (a) Outline the blood supply and drainage in the mammal of: (i) the villi of the small intestine and (ii) the Malpighian bodies (renal corpuscles) of the kidney. (4)
(b) Describe the changes occurring in the blood during its passage through the villi and the Malpighian bodies. (10)
(c) State under what circumstances the blood flow to the small intestine is altered. (4)
(*Cambridge International A, 1990*)

4. Give reasoned physiological explanations of the following statements.
(a) People produce larger volumes of dilute urine on a cold day than on a hot day. (3)
(b) If blood pressure drops, as a result of blood loss in serious injury, urine production almost stops. (3)
(c) Protein may be detected in the urine of a person suffering from kidney failure. (3)
(*London A, 1990*)

5. (a) Give an account of how the human heart rate is regulated. (12)
(b) Explain how a person's way of life may influence the occurrence of coronary heart disease. (8)
(*Cambridge Social Biology A, 1990*)

6. For each of the following features associated with gas exchange, describe its precise location and state one of its functions: pleura, intercostal muscle, diaphragm and respiratory centre. (8)
(*London AS, 1990*)

7. (a) Explain why, in order to see an object most clearly under conditions of dim light, one should look to one side of the object and not directly at it. (2)
(b) The retina contains three types of cone cells sensitive to either red or blue or green wavelengths of light. Explain how the brain is able to: (i) perceive the colour yellow and (ii) distinguish between shades of a colour. (4)
(*JMB, Human and Social Biology AS, 1989*)

8. Discuss mechanisms in humans for the regulation of: (i) body temperature and (ii) blood glucose concentration. (15)
(*Scotland, Higher Grade, 1990 Specimen*)

9. (a) Describe the structure of a neurone as revealed by the light microscope. (5)
(b) Explain the following processes involved in the transmission of impulses along a neurone: (i) the formation of the resting membrane potential and (ii) the formation and transmission of an action potential. (10)
(c) How do retinal cells transduce light energy into nerve impulses? (5)
(*London A, 1990*)

10. Either **A** Discuss the effects of carbon dioxide on the transport of oxygen by haemoglobin.
Or **B** Describe how a nerve impulse is conducted along a motor neurone and explain the events that occur when the impulse reaches the motor end plate. (25)
(*COSSEC AS, 1990*)

11. Write an essay on one of the following topics:
(a) The structure and functions of the liver. (24)
(b) The mechanism and regulation of breathing. (24)
(*AEB Human biology A, 1990*)

ANSWERS TO TEXT QUESTIONS

■ CHAPTER 1 CELLS AND TISSUES

1. The epidermis of the skin exfoliates continuously, as do the gut epithelia and the epithelium lining the bronchial tree.

2. Photograph B shows the normal cells, and photograph A shows the smear containing malignant cells. The enlarged and irregular nuclei of the malignant cells are clearly visible, together with clumping of the cells and reduced amounts of cytoplasm.

3. Normal migratory cells include white blood cells, fibroblasts and embryonic cells.

4. Both liver cells and new neurones are formed by the type of cell division known as mitosis.

5. Rubella has a teratogenic effect in early pregnancy. If a pregnant woman has not previously been immunised, and catches the virus, there is a serious risk of fetal damage such as blindness, deafness, and heart defects.

6. Like the choroid, the pigmented epithelium behind the retina absorbs light, preventing internal reflection (see Chapter 7).

7. (a) In the bronchi the cilia waft dirt and bacteria trapped in the mucus up to the glottis, where it can be swallowed and disinfected by the stomach acid. Thus they keep the lungs and bronchial tree clean.
(b) In the oviducts, cilia have a transporting role. They waft sperm up to the oocyte for fertilisation, and waft oocytes (fertilised or unfertilised) down to the uterus.

8. In sunburn, harmful ultraviolet rays destroy cells in the epidermis, unless they are protected by melanin which absorbs these rays. (High factor suncream also absorbs, or 'filters out' the ultraviolet rays.) The skin feels hot and itchy because of localised reaction to tissue damage. The malpighian layer produces new living cells beneath the burned tissue and all the dead layers peel off together.

9. If the burn is extensive, then large amounts of plasma may leak out through the damaged skin, resulting in serious dehydration. The damaged skin also represents a break in the body's defences for the entry of opportunist bacteria.

10. The skin on the soles of the feet thickens in response to friction and to the distortion of the basal malpighian cells when they are subjected to the weight of the body. They are stimulated to divide faster and so increase the number of cell layers outside them. More alpha-keratin is also secreted which makes the tissue tougher.

11. 7.1μ m

12. Approximately 40%

13. Fetal haemoglobin has a greater affinity for oxygen than maternal haemoglobin in respiring tissues.

14. The curve for fetal haemoglobin will be to the left of the curves for adult haemoglobin.

15. Three factors that may cause hypoxia in the tissues are: reduced oxygen tension in the atmosphere, as could occur when climbing a high mountain, or when exercising at high altitudes; poor oxygen uptake across the alveolar surface, due to lung diseases such as pneumonia, emphysema or bronchitis; reduced red cell count, due to some form of anaemia.

16. Mr Brown was suffering from anaemia, caused by his poor diet.

17. Mr Brown's anaemia means that insufficient oxygen is reaching the tissues, so the level of erythropoietin in his blood will rise. The doctor could test for this to confirm the diagnosis.

18. This type of anaemia can easily be treated, by giving Mr Brown dietary supplements of iron, vitamin B_{12} and folic acid along with his cream buns.

19. Jaundice is common in newborn babies because fetal haemoglobin is efficient at exchange across the placenta, but much less efficient in the alveoli and tissues, so fetal red cells must be broken down as quickly as possible and replaced with cells containing adult haemoglobin.

20. Children are immunised against diphtheria, whooping cough and tetanus (bacterial infections), and measles, polio and rubella (viral infections).

21. Dogs may be immunised against distemper, hard pad, leptospirosis, hepatitis and possibly kennel cough. Cats may be immunised against feline enteritis and cat flu.

22. The role of the helper T-cells is to enhance the manufacture of antibodies by the B-cells. The HIV virus will therefore make the immune response less effective, and the AIDS sufferer will become 'immuno-deficient'. He or she may become seriously ill from any number of infections which would be trivial under normal circumstances.

23. The antibodies in the plasma of the donated blood will be greatly diluted on entering the recipient's bloodstream. They may damage a few red cells but not enough to cause a blockage.

24. There is unlikely to be a problem. At this age, the baby's immune system is not developed enough to respond to its mother's antigens.

25. Haemostasis stops excessive bleeding, or haemorrhage; it prevents the entry of infective agents such as viruses and bacteria; and it forms a base for tissue repair.

■ CHAPTER 2 SUPPORT AND MOVEMENT

1. Athletic qualities include: lean body with low fat to muscle ratio, powerful muscles with good muscle tone, long legs are useful so centre of gravity of body can be further forward when running, efficient heart with slow pulse rate, stamina, from raised myoglobin content and adequate stores of glycogen.

2. He could improve his performance by training, preferably at altitude, and possibly with weights. A high carbohydrate diet just before the race will help raise glycogen levels.

3. Locomotion is important for: finding a mate, dispersal and migration, foraging for food, hunting, escape from predators, danger, etc.

4. The fact that each muscle fibre can respond separately allows for a wide range of responses. Muscle actions can be subject to fine tuning.

5. The wave of contraction spreads through the conducting system of branched fibres, via the gap junctions in the intercalated discs.

6. The acetylcholine is very quickly broken down by the enzyme acetylcholine esterase.

7. Red muscle is affected first, since white muscles has a more extensive sarcoplasmic reticulum.

8. For the reaction of myosin with actin to occur, ATP, ATPase and calcium ions must be present.

9. The scapula must be fixed, as must the elbow joint.

10. Effort = 84 kg.

11. Maximum load = 1080 kg (as heavy as a small car).

12. The hardening of the costal, tracheal and bronchial cartilages would make ventilation movements more laboured. The hardening of the articular cartilages would make joints stiffer and less flexible.

13. As the thumb presses the teeth forwards, the increased pressure in front stimulates osteoclast activity and bone absorption, while the reduced pressure behind the teeth stimulates osteoblast activity and bone formation. The teeth are thus moved forwards. A dental brace reverses these forces and cell activities, returning the teeth to their correct position.

14. A pair of ill-fitting shoes can result in deformed bones in young feet. This will contribute to problems of bunions and corns in later life.

15. Vitamin D deficiency could result from poor diet, or from a lack of sunlight to stimulate its production in the skin. (Either due to atmospheric pollution, or to keeping all of the skin covered out of doors as required by some cultures). Fish liver oils are a good source of dietary vitamin D.

16. In rickets, the ossification of bone in growing children is hindered, so bone remains soft. When the child tries to walk, the weight-bearing bones of the legs, pelvis and spine will bend or become deformed.

17. To move the same load, the effort would be only 28 kg, so it would be more efficient mechanically. This does not happen however, since it would make the fore-limb such an unwieldy shape that movement would actually be less easy so it would be selectively disadvantageous.

18. *Long bones*: femur, tibia, fibula, metatarsals, humerus, radius, ulna, metacarpals.
Short bones: vertebrae, tarsals, carpals.
Flat bones: pelvis, scapula, clavicle, ribs, cranial bones.
Irregular bones: sternum, patella, bones of middle ear.

19. *Advantage*: the gaps between the bones mean that the head can be squashed as it passes down the birth canal, making the delivery of the baby quicker (and so safer for the baby), and more comfortable for the mother.
Disadvantage: the head of a young baby is very vulnerable until the gaps (fontanelles) have closed up.

■ CHAPTER 3 TRANSPORT SYSTEMS

1. No. Each patient must be assessed to decide if the information would benefit, confuse or frighten them.

2. The left ventricle wall must pump blood all round the body whereas the right ventricle wall only pumps blood through the lungs. Thus more cardiac muscle is required in the left ventricle wall.
   The valves prevent backflow of blood: semilunar valves from arches to ventricles, tricuspid valve from right ventricle to right atrium, bicuspid valve from left ventricle to left atrium.

3. Blood volume = $(100 \times 60)/1000 = 6$ dm^3.

4. Average daily volume = $6 \times 60 \times 24 = 8640$ dm^3 day^{-1}.

5. The cardiac output increases during physical exercise for example, or in conditions of stress.

6. Damage to the mitral valve would make the emptying and filling of the left ventricle ineffective, so impairing the systemic circulation. Less oxygen, etc will reach the tissues, resulting in distress and weakness.

7. Beats per year = $72 \times 60 \times 24 \times 365$
$\qquad\qquad\qquad = 37.84 \times 10^6$.
In 70 years = 2649.02×10^6 beats.

8. Refer to page 6.

9. Refer to page 81.

10. The distance between 'P' and the 'QRS' complex would be lengthened.

11. (a) venous return would increase by the same amount, (b) cardiac muscle fibres stretch more, (c) arterial blood pressure increases, (d) venous blood pressure increases.

12. Beta-blockers lower blood pressure.

13. Fainting does not normally occur because the carotid and aortic baroreceptors immediately compensate.

14. Increased water content increases the blood volume and hence increases blood pressure, and vice versa.

15. Stroke volume = (15.6 x 1000)/120 = 130 cm^3. This would cause blood pressure to rise.

16. The fenestrated capillaries facilitate the processes of: (a) nutrient absorption in the villi, (b) ultrafiltration in the glomeruli, (c) uptake of iodine and release of hormones in the thyroid gland.

17. Fall in blood pressure would: (a) stop ultrafiltration in the glomeruli, (b) reduce gas exchange in the alveoli, (c) reduce oxygen and glucose supply to the brain, resulting in fainting.

18. (a) and (b) Both dehydration and a higher red cell count would make blood more viscous and hence increase blood pressure, (c) a reduction in plasma proteins would make blood less viscous and hence decrease blood pressure.

19. (a) Plaques would increase blood pressure in the vessel. (b) Plaques in the coronary arteries would reduce oxygen and glucose supply to cardiac muscle and so reduce the pumping effectiveness of the heart. (c) A thrombus might block the vessel; in coronary vessels this would cause a heart attack, in cerebral vessels it would cause a stroke. (d) A diet that is high in fat and cholesterol content.

20. (a) *Lung* capillaries - venules - pulmonary vein - left atrium - mitral valve - left ventricle - aortic semilunar valve - aortic arch - aorta -
either hepatic artery - arterioles - *liver* capillaries
or mesenteric artery arterioles - *ileum* capillaries - venules - hepatic portal vein - venules - *liver* capillaries.
Then liver venules - hepatic vein - posterior vena cava - right atrium - tricuspid valve - right ventricle - pulmonary semilunar valve - pulmonary arch - pulmonary artery - arterioles - *lung* capillaries.

21. Left subclavian vein.

22. The hepatic portal vein has an important role in homeostasis. It carries blood containing the products of protein and carbohydrate digestion direct to the liver, where the amino acid and glucose content of the blood is regulated so that the rest of the body receives relatively constant amounts. The brain is particularly sensitive to fluctuating glucose levels, and excess amino acids can be toxic. The hepatic vein blood will contain higher levels of urea and of hydrogencarbonate than the hepatic portal vein, but probably lower levels of glucose and amino acids.

23. (a) Blood remains enclosed within blood vessels, and even in the veins there is sufficient residual pressure to return blood to the heart. Tissue fluid is derived from liquid 'leaking' out of blood capillaries, and if draining is poor it may well collect within tissues and cause swelling. Mrs Morris stands still for several hours, and her problem is due to the combined effect of gravity and the lack of muscle contraction in her legs to help keep the lymph moving.
(b) An alternative (better?) treatment could be a programme of exercises that Mrs Morris could do while she is working, e.g. standing on tiptoe and down again several times.

■ CHAPTER 4 BREATHING SYSTEMS

1. Nosebleeds are common because of the extensive blood supply which is *just* under the surface of the nasal mucosa. The ice cools the blood in the external carotid arteries resulting in vasoconstriction and reduction of blood flow to the mucosa.

2. At the start of inspiration, the lung air pressure is lower than atmospheric, so air is pulled in through the trachea increasing the pressure. At the start of expiration, the pressure exceeds atmospheric, as air is forced out.

3. Lack of surfactant makes it hard to inflate the lungs and thus inspiration cannot be carried out efficiently. The baby has to be maintained on a ventilator.

4. Pressure in the pleural cavity becomes more negative, since the volume is increasing.

5. As air entered the pleural cavity, the lung would collapse, due to the elastic tissue of the lungs and the surface tension of the alveolar fluids (which still exists even with the effects of surfactants). Luckily the left and right pleural cavities are separate, so unless both sides are punctured, only one lung will collapse and the person can survive. The pleura may be punctured deliberately after lung surgery to allow the lung tissues time to heal, which they cannot do if they are stretching and contracting continually in ventilation.

6. The expired air actually consists of air from the alveoli mixed with air in the 'dead space'. The dead space air thus alters the composition of the alveolar air on exhalation.

7. When blood reaches respiring tissues, the pO_2 will decrease, as haemoglobin unloads oxygen to the respiring tissues. The pCO_2 will rise, as CO_2 is a product of respiration and diffuses from tissues to the blood.

8. It is dangerous to inhale large amounts of CO, because when it binds on to the haemoglobin, forming carboxyhaemoglobin, it prevents oxygen uptake (as the CO combines with the haemoglobin strongly whereas oxygen combines loosely). Thus death may occur.

9. (a) The lower ambient pO_2 at high altitudes means that oxygen uptake into the blood would be reduced.
(b) This would be sensed at the kidneys causing release of erythropoietin factor which would invoke the erythropoietin mechanism to increase red cell formation. It takes about five days to see a change in the red cell count, and about three weeks to become fully acclimatised.

10. For an adult at rest, volume of air breathed in one minute = tidal volume x breath frequency = 500 x 12 = 6 dm^3.

11. The remaining 150 cm^3 stays in the anatomical dead space.

12. (a) The vital capacity, which is the volume of exchangeable air, would decrease (b) The residual volume, which cannot be directly exchanged, would increase.

13. (a) 1% CO_2 would cause increased frequency of breathing. (b) 3% CO_2 would cause increased depth of breathing. (c) 6% CO_2 would cause death, due to failure to remove enough CO_2 from the body.

14. (a) High levels of lactate cause the blood pH to fall, thus more rapid ventilation. (b) This means that more O_2 is taken in to reduce the effects due to oxygen debt.

15. A striated muscle fibre is a syncytium consisting of a mass of sarcoplasm and nuclei rather than separate cells bathed by tissue fluid. This means that there is a long diffusion gradient into the muscle along which the oxygen must travel to reach the mitochondria.

16. It has this structure as the contractile proteins can be arranged more effectively for contraction.

■ CHAPTER 5 WATER BALANCE AND EXCRETION

1. This volume is greater than the total blood volume, which is only 6 dm^3.

2. To counteract dehydration, it is best to drink salt and sugar and water. The salt replaces depleted electrolytes, while the sugar helps them to be absorbed into the bloodstream.

3. The cramp is caused by salt imbalance in the muscles. They therefore need to drink a dilute salt solution to replace salt as well as water. This is not as unpleasant as it sounds, when your body is really lacking in salt, a pinch of salt in a glass of water actually tastes 'sweety'!

4. The male urethra is proportionally much longer since it extends through the penis. It also passes through the prostate gland. Otherwise the two urinary systems are the same.

5. The route is as follows: *renal artery* - lobar artery - arcuate artery - afferent arteriole - glomerulus - efferent arteriole - vasa recta - venule - arcuate vein - lobar vein - *renal vein*.

6. If the flow rate is 125 cm^3 per minute, then the kidneys will produce 180 dm^3 of glomerular filtrate per day. Calculation: (125 x 60 x 24)/1000.

7. The plasma volume is 55% of the total blood volume, i.e. 0.55 x 6 = 3.3 dm^3. So the number of times the plasma is filtered in a day = 180/3.3 = 54 times.

8. (a) The urine volume will increase, and it will become more dilute. (b) The coffee is unlikely to quench your thirst in the long run, as the extra loss of water in your urine will balance the water absorbed in your gut. Incidentally, as most hangover symptoms are caused by dehydration, the traditional 'black coffee to sober up' may well make the sufferer feel worse!

9. (a) Diabetes insipidus results in an increased volume of very dilute urine, and a decreased volume of more concentrated blood. (b) The current treatment is by regular injection of ADH (vasopressin).

10. Advantages of home dialysis include: less risk of cross-infection with other patients; less disruption to family life by not having to attend hospital at precise hours on a rigid basis. Disadvantages include: the home water supply may be more variable than that of the dialysis department, and water purification units are expensive; there is always the posibility of a power cut at home, which could be fatal if it occurred while dialysis was being carried out. (Hospitals have emergency generators which take over as soon as the national grid supply is cut off.)

11. He could only make a full recovery if a suitable donor kidney became available and he had a kidney transplant.

12. (a) They could be immunised against hepatitis. (b) HIV is transmitted in blood, so they could be exposed to AIDS.

■ CHAPTER 6 FOOD AND NUTRITION

1. Other problem ingredients to which some people may be sensitive include egg proteins, proteins in beef and in certain nuts, and lactose, the main sugar in milk. Some food additives also cause adverse reactions. These include colourings such as tartrazine (E102), which has been linked with hyperactivity in children, preservatives such as potassium benzoate (E212), which should be avoided by asthmatics and aspirin-sensitive people, and antioxidants such as BHA (E320) which is not permitted in baby and infant food.

2. In a balanced diet, energy intake usually exceeds energy expenditure because the food eaten will contain some dietary fibre that cannot be digested and absorbed, so will not contribute to the energy used in the body. It is also difficult to quantify the energy that is lost as heat, in maintaining the body temperature, and in expired air and other excreta.

3. People who are obese are likely to have fat deposited around their heart and within their arteries. Their heart must therefore work much harder to pump blood round the body, and heart attack becomes more likely. (See also Chapter 3 for further information about the heart.)

4. The 'typical' Western diet contains excess fat to start with, and also tends to be low in dietary fibre because we eat so many processed foods, and foods made from 'refined' white flour. Fibre absorbs cholesterol in the gut, preventing it from being absorbed into the bloodstream.

5. The Inuit obtain the glucose they need from non-carbohydrate sources, e.g. amino acids. This is known as *gluconeogenesis* and occurs in the liver.

6. All protein that we eat is digested to amino acids which are absorbed into the blood. The liver deaminates any amino acids that are surplus to requirements. This involves the removal of the amino part of the molecule which is then converted into urea. The remaining portion is converted into a keto acid which can be used as a respiratory substrate.

7. The vegetable oils used in the manufacture of margarines are solidified by a process of hydrogenation i.e. breaking the double bond between the carbon atoms in the fatty acid hydrocarbon chain and saturating the molecule with hydrogens. The degree of hydrogenation determines how solid the margarine is at room temperature. Manufacturers in countries like Australia produce a margarine for the hot summer months which contains a high proportion of hydrogenated vegetable oils, and a margarine for the winter months which is not hydrogenated to the same extent.

8. The energy yield per gram for carbohydate is approximately half that for fat. This means that the Inuit would have to consume 600 grams of carbohydrate daily to replace 300 grams of fat. In the Arctic tundra regions, staple carbohydrate crops such as wheat, maize and rice, obviously cannot grow, so it would be extremely difficult and expensive for Inuits to obtain that amount of carbohydrate.

9. A stratified epithelium would be a major disadvantage in the stomach, small intestine and colon, as it would prevent absorption of nutrients.

10. The stomach acid would eventually damage the mucosa in the oesophagus, leading to ulceration.

11. The peptic cells occur low down in the tubular glands where there are no goblet cells to secrete protective mucus. If the proteolytic gastric enzymes were secreted in an active form, they could digest the cells that make them.

12. Stress could cause ulcers because with stress, adrenaline levels are high, and this stimulates acid secretion in the stomach leading to erosion or ulceration.

13. Ulcers can be prevented in people at risk by reducing stress and getting sufficient rest. Such people should also not smoke or drink, as both nicotine and alcohol stimulate acid secretion.

14. If part of the stomach has been removed, the individual's feeding habits would change by having to eat smaller meals, perhaps more frequently.

15. Emulsification means reducing the surface tension on fat globules, and is a function of the soaps formed in the duodenum. Large globules are thus split up into small ones, increasing the surface area for the action of lipase enzymes.

16. A person with no gall bladder should consume a low-fat diet, with an added dietary supplement of EFA.

17. The Golgi body will receive the fat in vesicles that have been pinched off from the smooth endoplasmic reticulum. It will 'package' the fat by adding the protein coat, and Golgi vesicles will carry the coated fat to the plasma membrane for secretion from the cell.

■ CHAPTER 7 CO-ORDINATION AND CONTROL

1. EEG (b) shows the epileptic attack, because all the elctrodes show spike activity. In EEG (a), only 6 out of the 16 traces are particularly active. The electrical discharges are also much greater in EEG (b) than in EEG (a).

2. At point Q, the electrode traces are stabilising, so Jean seems to be recovering from her attack, either of her own accord, or possibly because she is receiving treatment.

3. (a) Frogs overwinter in the mud at the bottom of pools, where freezing will not occur.
(b) Butterflies overwinter as pupae which remain dormant and do not develop until warm conditions return.
(c) Hedgehogs hibernate, with a reduced body temperature and metabolic rate.

4. A slightly raised temperature speeds up the immune response and phagocytosis. The optimum temperature for the growth of pathogenic bacteria is probably 37°C, so a higher temperature should impede their growth and multiplication.

5. (a) Behavioural responses to overheating include: seeking shade, moulting or shedding clothes, lying extended to present a large surface area for heat loss, panting to increase ventilatory heat loss.
(b) Behavioural responses to chilling include: lying in the sun, curling up to present a small surface area for heat loss, huddling together for warmth, wearing more clothes or growing a winter coat.

6. (a) The optic nerve is myelinated, since signals from visual stimuli must pass rapidly to the brain.
(b) Sciatic motor fibres are myelinated, since rapid signals to muscles are required in order to allow rapid responses to stimuli.
(c) Gut muscle nerves are non-myelinated, since only slow responses and contraction occur in the visceral muscle undergoing peristalsis.

7. Monoamine oxidase acts as an anti-depressant, because it allows the build up of adrenaline and noradrenaline, thus raising blood glucose levels, improving ventilation efficiency and stimulating mental awareness.

8. Curare prevents acetylcholine attaching to the ACh receptors on the sarcolemma of striated muscles. This results in paralysis, and as the intercostal muscles and diaphragm are paralysed, the person dies from asphyxiation.

9. In a voluntary arc, there is only one motor neurone and one relay neurone in the grey matter. In an autonomic arc, there are two motor neurones, a preganglionic one which synapses in the ganglion with a postganglionic neurone. There is no relay fibre.

10. The white matter contains myelinated fibres. These run long distances up and down the CNS, so it is essential that they conduct quickly. The grey matter contains non-myelinated fibres. These conduct slowly, but since they only pass relatively short distances, e.g. from dorsal root to ventral root, the time involved is still small.

11. (a) The speech area is located in the left frontal lobe (Broca's area).
(b) Severe dizziness suggests damage in the cerebellum, where balance is co-ordinated.
(c) An abnormal heart rhythm means that the medulla oblongata has been damaged.
(d) General left-sided paralysis indicates that damage has occurred in the right side of brain, either in the cerebellum or cerebrum.

12. Receptors include: rods and cones in the retina; hair cells in the cochlea; taste cells in the taste buds on the tongue, gums and cheeks, olfactory cells for smell in the nasal mucosa; pressure receptors in the skin.

13. In a myopic eye, the image is in sharp focus in front of the retina. This is corrected with a concave lens. In a hypermetropic eye, the image is in sharp focus behind the retina. This is corrected with a convex lens.

14. The retina is described as inverted, because light has to penetrate through all the ancillary neurones before reaching the rods and cones.

15. (a) Audiogram A from Library Lil shows a normal response, while audiogram B from Disco Dan shows considerable hearing loss of 40 dB around middle C (256 cycles s^{-1}) and up to 90 dB at higher frequencies, with both ears affected. Dan must have been exposed to very loud noise for considerable lengths of time and has probably been standing too close to the disco speaker.
(b) Most speech is around 40 to 50 dB so Dan would not hear it at all. He will require a hearing aid for the rest of his life. Lil can hear speech.

16. The endolymph in the vestibular apparatus goes on moving for a short while after the body movement has stopped, so the cristae and maculae are still being stimulated. Impulses are still being sent to the brain which is sending impulses to the appropriate muscles, including the external eye muscles, to balance the apparent movement.

17. The cerebellum is the part of the brain concerned with posture and balance.

18. Growth hormone treatment must be given while young, because once epiphyseal plates have closed the bones are fully ossified and cannot grow any more.

19. GH is not administered by mouth because it is a protein, and would be digested and destroyed.

20. Bioengineered GH is now readily available, made by recombinant DNA technology.

21. GH in milk is unlikely to pose a health risk, as the levels are low, and it will be destroyed by digestion.

22. Osteoclasts are the cells that cause bone breakdown, and osteoblasts are responsible for the build up new bone tissue.

23. For cretinism, symptoms include mental retardation and slow physical development, so that the child remains a dwarf. In myxoedema, the patient is lethargic and lacks mental alertness. They have a reduced cardiac output and put on weight. (b) Symptoms can be alleviated by giving thyroxine, which can be taken by mouth.

24. Lack of dietary iodine means low blood levels of iodine, so the hypothalamus will be continually stimulated to release TRF. The anterior pituitary continually releases TSH, so the thyroid tissue is stimulated over a long period and thus enlarges.

25. About 100 g of glycogen are stored in the human liver and another 20 g in striated muscle.

26. Only Claud is suffering from sugar diabetes. He shows a response that is elevated even over the renal threshold, which is why glucose appears in his urine. Mary's levels do not exceed the threshold and are normal.

27. In Mary's case, it is probably the pressure of her baby on her kidneys that is causing the urinary glucose loss (this is quite normal in pregnancy).

28. Most sugar diabetics now use bioengineered insulin (human).

29. No, sleeping is not stressful. On the contrary, sleep is a process that actually relieves stress, partly by causing the release of anti-stress hormones.

■ CHAPTER 8 REPRODUCTION

1. *For*: Allowing this research to be done will lead to a better understanding of early human development and of genetic defects, and enough knowledge may be gained to treat the defects effectively, or to avoid their occurrence. It may lead to a better understanding of infertility and spontaneous abortion.
Against: Many people feel that human life is sacrosanct and that at some time during early development, perhaps when the zygote is initially formed, the soul also enters the embryo.

2. Meiosis is important because it reduces the diploid state ($2n$) to the haploid state (n) which thus compensates for the doubling effect of fertilisation on the chromosome number. It also introduces genetic variation to the gametes which may be of selective value.

3. Secondary sexual characteristics in men include the growth of body hair, especially on the face, deepening of the voice due to a wider larynx, development of a more muscular body and narrower hips.

4. Artificial insemination involves the placing of active semen close to the cervix of, for example, a cow at the time of oestrous. It is injected through a tube inserted up the vagina by a skilled operator or veterinary surgeon. This procedure has a number of advantages. The semen can have been obtained from a bull that has been suitably 'progeny tested', i.e. one that has sired calves that develop excellent traits, such as quick growth rate or good milk yield. This is less 'hit and miss' than allowing a non-progeny tested bull to fertilise the cows in the herd. It is also a lot cheaper to transport semen from bull to cow than to bring the animals themselves together, and it avoids the problem that the prospective 'parents' may not co-operate and perform to order!

5. If the embryo implanted close to the cervix, the placenta may well develop between the baby and the cervix (placenta previa), so blocking the birth canal. Since the baby must be born before the placenta is detached, a Caesarian section to remove the baby would then need to be carried out.

6. If amniocentesis had been carried out when Mrs Thomas was pregnant with Andy, his Down's syndrome would have been easy to diagnose. The cells in the amniotic fluid are removed by centrifugation and suitably stained. The chromosomes in the nucleus are photographed, then the photograph is cut up so that the 23 pairs of chromosomes can be arranged in order, from the largest to the smallest. In Down's syndrome, there is an extra chromosome number 21 (hence 'trisomy 21'), due to non-disjunction of the 21st pair of chromosomes in either the oocyte or sperm. (For further details on human genetics see *Biology Advanced Studies - Genetics*.)

7. Identical twins result from a single egg fertilised by a single sperm. The zygote then divides into two separate cells from which two individuals develop. Non-identical twins result if two eggs are released at ovulation, and both are fertilised successfully.

8. Fetal haemoglobin has a higher affinity for oxygen than maternal haemoglobin at the pO_2 tensions in the placenta. Thus as oxygen is off-loaded from the maternal haemoglobin it diffuses to the fetal haemoglobin which on-loads and removes it, so maintaining the diffusion gradient.

9. Once the amnion is ruptured, the cushioning amniotic fluid is lost (i.e. the 'waters' have broken), so the baby is pressing directly on the endometrial lining. This increases the stimulation to the hypothalamus to release more and more oxytocin, and the raised oxytocin levels increase the intensity and duration of the contractions.

10. If a newborn baby is HIV positive, the antibody must have come from the mother via the placenta, as newborn babies have little ability to produce antibodies themselves. The mother must therefore be infected with the AIDS virus although it may not be in an active stage. The baby may or may not be infected, since it is possible that the antibodies only have crossed the placenta. If after a few months the baby is HIV negative it is unlikely to have the virus.

11. Breastfeeding establishes an early and prolonged contact and bonding between mother and baby. It promotes good development of jaw and facial muscles and teeth. The baby itself is in control of intake. The constituents of human milk are more suited to the baby than those of cows' milk, e.g. fats and iron can be better absorbed and the amino acids more readily metabolised. The lower sodium content of human milk is more suited to the baby. The colostrum provides important antibodies to the baby which prevent gastroenteritis, and reduce the danger of respiratory infections and meningitis. There is less likelihood of an allergic reaction towards human milk. Milk of mothers with premature babies has a higher protein content than milk from full-term mothers, and this stimulates the growth of premature babies.

INDEX